W9-AON-356

# I
# COULDN'T
# HELP
# LAUGHING

# I COULDN'T HELP
# LAUGHING stories

## elected and introduced by
## GDEN NASH

. B. LIPPINCOTT COMPANY   Philadelphia • New York

## ACKNOWLEDGMENTS

The editor and publisher wish
to express their appreciation for
permission given them to reprint
the following selections:

"Ask me a Question," from *Benchley Beside Himself* by Robert Benchley. Copyright, 1930, by Robert C. Benchley. Reprinted by permission of Harper & Brothers.

"Father Is Firm with His Ailments," reprinted from *Life with Father* by
Clarence Day, by permission of Alfred A. Knopf, Inc. Copyright
1933, 1935 by Clarence Day. Originally published in *The New Yorker*.

"Statement of Arthur James Wentworth, Bachelor of Arts," from *The
Vexations of A. J. Wentworth, B.A.* by Humphrey F. Ellis. Per-
mission of the author, Little Brown & Co., and Evans Brothers, Ltd.
Copyright 1941, 1942, 1945, 1946, by Bradbury Agnew & Co., Ltd.
Copyright 1950, by Little, Brown and Company.

"The Burglars," reprinted from *The Golden Age* by Kenneth Grahame
by permission of Dodd, Mead & Company and John Lane The
Bodley Head, Ltd.

"An Unsavoury Interlude," from *Stalky & Co.*, by Rudyard Kipling,
reprinted by permission of Mrs. George Bambridge, Doubleday &
Company, Inc., and The Macmillan Company of Canada.

"Horseshoes," reprinted by permission of Mrs. Lardner from *How to
Write Short Stories* by Ring Lardner. Copyright 1952 by Ellis A.
Lardner.

"My Financial Career," reprinted by permission of Dodd, Mead & Company from *The Leacock Roundabout* by Stephen Leacock and by
permission of McClelland & Stewart, Ltd., Canada, from *Laugh With
Leacock* by Stephen Leacock.

"Stranger in the House" by Ogden Nash. Copyright © 1954 by Ogden
Nash. Originally published in *The New Yorker*.

"Frou-Frou, or the Future of Vertigo," from *Look Who's Talking* by
S. J. Perelman. Copyright 1937, 1938, 1939, 1940 by S. J. Perelman,
published by Random House, Inc.; reprinted by permission of the
author. Originally published in *The New Yorker*.

"The Schartz-Metterklume Method," from *The Short Stories of Saki
(H. H. Munro)*, copyright 1930 by The Viking Press, Inc.; by per-
mission of the publishers, The Viking Press, Inc., and John Lane The
Bodley Head, Ltd.

Chapter IV, *Our Hearts Were Young and Gay*, reprinted by permission
of Dodd, Mead & Company from *Our Hearts Were Young and Gay*
by Cornelia Otis Skinner and Emily Kimbrough. Copyright © 1942
by Dodd, Mead & Company, Inc.

"Crisp New Bills for Mr. Teagle" by Frank Sullivan. Copyright ©
1935 by The New Yorker Magazine, Inc. By permission of the
author.

"Miss Rennsdale Accepts," from *Penrod* by Booth Tarkington. Doubleday & Company, Inc. Copyright 1913, 1941, by Booth Tarkington.
Reprinted by permission of Brandt & Brandt.

"More Alarms at Night" by James Thurber. Copyright © 1933 by The
New Yorker Magazine, Inc. By permission of the author.

"Philip Wedge," from *Quo Vadimus?* by E. B. White. Copyright, 1929,
1957, by E. B. White. Reprinted by permission of the author and
Harper & Brothers. Originally published in *The New Yorker*.

"Uncle Fred Flits By," from *Young Men in Spats* by P. G. Wodehouse.
Reprinted by permission of the author and Herbert Jenkins, Ltd.
Copyright, 1931, 1933, 1934, 1935 by Pelham Granville Wodehouse.

# FOREWORD

I wish hereby to scotch the rumor
That I'd attempt to write on humor,
For those who do, fall into groups
Of solemn pompous nincompoops
By whom a joke must be enjoyed
In terms of Bergson or of Freud.
Portentously they probe and test,
And in the jargon lose the jest.
True humor can't be taught in schools,
For wayward humor knows no rules,
So do not spoil your present laughter
By trying to analyze it after.

Humor, I read somewhere, and ceased,
Divides the human from the beast.
My comment on this thought is, Rats!
I've been laughed at by dogs and cats;
Inanimate objects rock with glee
As they conspire to baffle me.
No, no, the way the cards are cut,
Nature's the jester, man the butt,
Which simply leaves it up to us
To admit that we're ridiculous;
To view us with irreverent eyes
And grin when whittled down to size.

There follows not a single story
To hymn the human race's glory,
But rather a posy of pieces antic,
Indigenous and trans-Atlantic,
Which smile at human folly and foible.
I hope that you will find them enjoible.

*Ogden Nash*

# CONTENTS

## ASK ME A QUESTION by Robert Benchley

PROFESSORS in our universities are getting awfully nosey of late. They are always asking questions or sending out questionnaires inquiring into your private life. I can remember the day when all that a professor was supposed to do was to mark "C minus" on students' examination papers and then go home to tea. Nowadays they seem to feel that they must know just how much we (outside the university) eat, what we do with our spare time, and how we like our eggs. I, for one, am inclined not to tell any more. I already have filled in enough stuff on questionnaires to get myself divorced or thrown into jail.

A particularly searching series of questions has just come from an upstate university trying to find out about my sleeping habits. The director of the psychological laboratory wants to know a lot of things which, if I were to give them out, would practically put me in the position of sleeping in John Wanamaker's window. I would have no more privacy than Irvin Cobb.

The first question is a simple one: "How many hours do you sleep each night, on the average?"

Well, professor, that would be hard to say. I might

add "and what's it to you?" but I suppose there must be some reason for wanting to know. I can't imagine any subject of less general interest than the number of hours I sleep each night on the average. No one has ever given a darn before, and I must say that I am rather touched at this sudden display of interest on the part of a stranger. Perhaps if I were to tell him that I hardly sleep at all he would come down and read to me.

But I would like to bet that the professor gets a raft of answers. If there is one thing that people like to talk about it is their sleeping habits. Just get a group started telling how much or how little they sleep each night and you will get a series of personal anecdotes which will put the most restless member of the party to sleep in no time.

"Well, it's a funny thing about me," one will say. "I get to bed, we'll say, at 11:30, and I go to sleep the minute my head hits the pillow and sleep right through until 7:30."

He will be interrupted at this point by some one who insists on having it known that the night before he heard the clock strike 2, 3, and 4. (People always seem to take a great deal of pride in having heard the clock strike 2, 3, and 4. You will seldom find one who admits having slept soundly all through the night. Just as a man will never admit that the suit he has on is new, so is he loath to confess that he is a good sleeper. I don't understand it, but, as I am getting pretty old now, I don't much care.)

You will be lucky if, in an experience meeting of this

kind, you don't start some one off telling the dream he had a few nights ago.

"It was the darndest thing," some one will say, as the rest pay no attention, but try to think up dreams they themselves have had recently, "it was the darndest thing. I seemed to be in a sort of big hall, only it wasn't exactly a hall either; it was more of a rink or schoolhouse. It seemed that Harry was there and all of a sudden instead of Harry it was Lindbergh. Well, so we all were going to a football game or something and I had on my old gray suit, except that it had wheels on it——"

By this time everybody is engaged in lighting cigarettes or looking at newspapers or even talking to some one else in a low tone of voice, and the narrator of the dream has practically no one to listen to him except the unfortunate who happens to be sitting next. But he doesn't seem to care and goes right on, until he has finished. There is a polite murmur of "What had you been eating?" or "That certainly was a corker," and then some one else starts. The professor who sent this questionnaire will have to watch out for this sort of thing or he will be swamped.

The whole list is just a temptation to garrulousness. Question No. 3, for example, is likely to get people started on an hour's personal disclosure. "Do you notice ill effects the day after sleeping on a train?" is the way it is worded.

Well, now take me for example. I'm glad you asked that, professor. I do notice ill effects the day after sleeping on a train. I notice, in the first place, that I haven't got my underthings buttoned correctly.

Dressing in a Pullman berth is, at best, a temporary form of arraying oneself, but if I happen to have to go right from the train to my engagement without going first to a hotel and doing the whole thing over again, I find, during the day, that I have buttoned the top button of my running drawers into the bottom buttonhole of my waistcoat and that one whole side of my shirt is clamped, by some mysterious process, half way up my back. This, as the day wears on, exerts a pull on the parts affected until there is grave danger of the whole body becoming twisted to the right, or left, as the case may be. This, in turn, leads to an awkward gait in walking and is likely to cause comment. Of course, if it is a strange town, people may think that you walk that way naturally and, out of politeness, say nothing about it, but among friends you are pretty sure to be accused of affectation or even worse.

Another ill effect, professor, which I feel after having slept on a Pullman (leaving aside the inevitable cold in the head acquired from sleeping with a light brown blanket piled high on one hip), is the strange appearance I present when I take my hat off.

As I am usually the last man in the washroom, I am constantly being harried by the porter, who keeps coming to the door and telling me that the train is pulling out into the yards in three minutes. (It is always three minutes, never less and never, by any chance, more.) Now, with this unpleasant threat hanging over me, I am in no state of mind to make my customary exquisite toilet. I brush my teeth and possibly shave one-half of my face, but almost invariably forget to brush my hair.

It is all right going through the station with my hat on, but later in the day, when I come to my business appointments, I notice that I am the object of considerable curious attention from people who do not know me, owing to my hair standing on end during an entire conference or even a luncheon. It is usually laid to my being a writer and of an artistic temperament, but it doesn't help me in a business way.

Now you will see what you got yourself into by merely asking me that one question, professor. I could go on like this for hours, telling about the ill effects I feel the day after sleeping in a Pullman, but maybe you aren't interested any longer. I am afraid I have bored you already.

The next question, however, is likely to start me off again. "Do you usually sleep through the night without awakening?"

It is funny that you should have asked that. I was just about to tell you anyway. Some nights I do, and some nights I don't. I can't be any more explicit than that.

When my little boys were small, I really can't say that I did. Not that they really meant to be mean about it, or did it deliberately, but, as I look back on it, it seems that there was always something. A glass of water was usually the ostensible excuse, but a great many times it turned out to be just a desire on their part to be chummy and have some one to cry with. I would say that, during the infancy of my bairn, my average was something like 10 complete arisings from bed during the night and 15 incomplete ones. By "incomplete" I mean those little starts out of a sound sleep, where one leg is thrust out from under the bedclothes while one waits to see if maybe the disturbance will not die down of its own accord.

These abortive arisings are really just as disturbing to the sleep as the complete ones, and should count as much in any scientific survey. (I do not want to convey the impression that I did all the hopping up during the night. The mother of the boys did her share, but it was a good two-man job on which turns had to be taken. It also depended a lot on which one could the better simulate sleep at the time of the alarm.)

Now that the boys are old enough to get up and get Daddy water when he wants it, things are a little different, but I find that the amount of undisturbed sleep that I get in one night's rest is dependent on so many outside factors that it is almost impossible to make up any statistics on the subject. A great deal of it depends on the neighbors and how much fun they happen to be having. Then there is the question of what tunes I've heard during the day. One good, monotonous tune firmly imbedded in my consciousness will make going to bed just a matter of form.

Two nights ago I retired early for a good rest (my first in nine years), but unfortunately spent seven out of my possible eight hours trying to get "What Is This Thing Called Love?" out of my mind. If I had only known some more of the words it wouldn't have been quite so bad, but one can't go on, hour after hour, mentally singing "What is this thing called love—what is this thing called love—what is this thing called love," without suffering some sort of nervous breakdown. It would have been much better for me to have been walking the streets than lying there in bed, plugging a song for nobody in particular.

It is this sort of thing which makes it difficult to answer Question No. 4. One night I am one way; the next night I am another way.

The only means that I can think of for the professor to employ to get an accurate check-up on my sleeping habits would be for him to come down to my place and sleep on an army cot at the foot of my bed himself. He would have to bring his own blankets, though, as I have hardly enough for myself as it is.

## FATHER IS FIRM WITH HIS AILMENTS by Clarence Day

FATHER got annoyed at us when we didn't stay well. He usually stayed well himself and he expected us to be like him, and not faint and slump on his hands and thus add to his burdens.

He was fearless about disease. He despised it. All this talk about germs, he said, was merely newfangled nonsense. He said that when he was a boy there had been no germs that he knew of. Perhaps invisible insects existed, but what of it? He was as healthy as they were. "If any damned germs want to have a try at me," he said, "bring 'em on."

From Father's point of view, Mother didn't know how to handle an ailment. He admired her most of the time and thought there was nobody like her; he often said to us boys, "Your mother is a wonderful woman;" but he always seemed to disapprove of her when she was ill.

Mother went to bed, for instance, at such times. Yet she didn't make noises. Father heard a little gasping moan sometimes, but she didn't want him to hear even that. Consequently he was sure she wasn't suffering. There was nothing to indicate it, he said.

The worse she felt, the less she ever said about it, and the harder it was for him to believe that there was anything really wrong with her. "He says he can't see why I stay in bed so long," she once wrote to me, when I was away, "but this colitis is a mean affair which keeps one perfectly flat. The doctor told him yesterday the meaning of colitis, but he said he 'had never heard of the damned thing, thank God.' He feels very abused that he should be 'so upset by people with queer things the matter with them and doctors all over the place.'" (Mother underlined the word "people.")

Even Mother's colds made him fretful. Whenever she had one, she kept going as long as she could, pottering about her room looking white and tired, with a shawl round her shoulders. But sometimes she had to give up and crawl into her bed.

Father pished and poohed to himself about this, and muttered that it was silly. He said Mother was perfectly healthy. When people thought they were ill, he declared, it didn't mean that there was anything the matter with them, it was merely a sign of weak character. He often told Mother how weak it was to give in to an ailment, but every time he tried to strengthen her character in this respect, he said she seemed to resent it. He never remembered to try except when she could hardly hold her head up. From his point of view, though, that was the very time that she needed his help.

He needed hers, too, or not exactly her help but her company, and he never hesitated to say so. When she was ill, he felt lost.

He usually came up from his office at about five or

six. The first thing he did was to look around the house to find Mother. It made his home feel queer and empty to him when she wasn't there.

One night about six o'clock he opened the door of her bedroom. There was no light except for a struggling little fire which flickered and sank in the grate. A smell of witch-hazel was in the air, mixed with spirits of camphor. On the bed, huddled up under an afghan, Mother lay still, in the dark.

"Are you there, Vinnie?" Father said, in a voice even louder than usual because of his not being sure.

Mother moaned, "Go away."

"What?" he asked, in astonishment.

"Go away. Oh, go 'way."

"Damnation!" he said, marching out.

"Clare!"

"What is it?"

"Won't you *ple-e-ease* shut my door again!"

Father ground his teeth and shut it with such a bang that it made Mother jump.

He told himself she had nothing the matter with her. She'd be all right in the morning. He ate a good dinner. Being lonely, he added an extra glass of claret and some toasted crackers and cheese. He had such a long and dull evening that he smoked two extra cigars.

After breakfast the next morning, he went to her bedroom again. The fire was out. Two worn old slippers lay on a chair. The gray daylight was cheerless. Father stood at the foot of Mother's bed, looking disconsolately at her because she wasn't well yet. He had no one to laugh at or quarrel with; his features were lumpy with gloom.

"What is it?" Mother asked in a whisper, opening her weary eyes.

"Nothing," he said loudly. "Nothing."

"Well, for mercy's sake, don't come in here looking like that, Clare," Mother begged.

"What do you mean? Looking like what?"

"Oh, go away!" Mother shrieked. "When people are sick, they like to see a smile or something. I never will get well if you stand there and stare at me that way! And shut my door quietly this time. And let me alone."

Outside her door, when I asked him how Mother was, he said with a chuckle: "She's all right again. She isn't out of bed yet, but she sounds much better this morning."

Father's own experiences in a sick-room had been very few. When he was in his early thirties, he had an attack of gout which lasted three weeks. From that time until he was seventy-four and had pneumonia, he had no other serious illnesses. He said illnesses were mostly imaginary and he didn't believe in them.

He even declared that his pneumonia was imaginary. "It's only some idea of that doctor's," he said. "Nothing the matter with me but a cold." Our regular physician had died, and this new man and two trained nurses had all they could do, at first, to keep Father in bed.

The new doctor had pale-blue eyes, a slight build, and a way of inwardly smiling at the persons he talked to. He had a strong will in crises, and he was one of the ablest physicians in town. Mother had chosen him, however, chiefly because she liked one of his female cousins.

When Father got worse, the doctor kept warning him that it really *was* pneumonia, and that if he wouldn't be tractable, he might not get over it—especially at seventy-four.

Father lay in bed glowering at him and said: "I didn't send for you, sir. You needn't stand there and tell me what you want me to do. I know all about doctors. They think they know a damned lot. But they don't. Give your pills and things to Mrs. Day—she believes in them. That's all I have to say. There's no need to continue this discussion. There's the door, sir. Goodbye."

But somehow the discussion kept on, and much to his surprise Father at last became convinced he was ill. The doctor, leaving him alone in his bedroom to digest the bad news, came out in the hall, anxious and tired, to have a few words with Mother. As they stood outside Father's door whispering quietly, they heard his voice from within. Apparently, now that he knew he was in trouble, his thoughts had turned to his God. "Have mercy!" they heard him shouting indignantly. "I say have mercy, damn it!"

Any sufferings that Father ever had he attributed solely to God. Naturally, he never thought for a moment that God could mean him to suffer. He couldn't imagine God's wishing to punish him either, for his conscience was clear. His explanation seemed to be that God was clumsy, not to say muddle-headed.

However, in spite of God and the doctor, Father got over pneumonia, just as, some forty years before, he had got over his gout. Only, in conquering his gout, he had had the help of a cane and a masseur called Old Lowndes.

While the gout was besieging him, Father sat in a big chair by the fire with his bad foot on a stool, armed with a cane which he kept constantly ready. Not that he used the cane to walk with. When he walked, he hopped around on his other foot, uttering strong howls of fury. But he valued his cane highly, and needed it, too, as a war club. He threatened the whole family with it. When visitors entered the room he brandished it fiercely at them, to keep them away from his toe.

Old Lowndes was allowed to approach nearer than others, but he was warned that if he made any mistakes that cane would come down on his head. Father felt there was no knowing what harm Lowndes might have done if he hadn't shaken his cane at him and made him take care. As it was, owing largely to this useful stick, Father got well.

This experience convinced him that any disease could be conquered by firmness.

When he had a cold, his method of dealing with it was to try to clear it out by main force, either by violently blowing his nose or, still better, by sneezing. Mother didn't like him to sneeze, he did it with such a roar. She said she could feel it half across the room, and she was sure it was catching. Father said this was nonsense. He said his sneezes were healthy. And presently we'd hear a hearty, triumphant blast as he sneezed again.

Aside from colds, which he had very seldom, his only foes were sick headaches. He said headaches only came from eating, however. Hence a man who knew enough to stop eating could always get rid of one that way. It took time to starve it out thoroughly. It might take several hours. But as soon as it was gone, he could eat again and enjoy his cigar.

When one of these headaches started, Father lay down and shut his eyes tight and yelled. The severity of a headache could be judged by the volume of sound he put forth. His idea seemed to be to show the head- ache that he was just as strong as it was, and stronger. When a headache and he went to bed together, they were a noisy pair.

Father's code required him to be game, I suppose. He never spoke or thought of having a code; he wasn't that sort of person; but he denounced men whose standards were low, as to gameness or anything else. It didn't occur to him to conceal his sufferings, however; when he had any pains, he expressed them as fully as he knew how. His way of being brave was not to keep still but to keep on fighting the headache.

Mother used to beg him to be quiet at night, even if he did have a headache, and not wake up the whole house. He never paid the slightest attention to such a request. When she said, "Please don't groan so much,

Clare," he'd look at her in disgust, as though he were a warrior being asked to stifle his battle-cries.

One evening he found Mother worrying because Aunt Emma was ill with some disease that was then epidemic.

"Oh, pooh!" Father said. "Nothing the matter with Emma. You can trust people to get any ailment whatever that's fashionable. They hear of a lot of other people having it, and the first thing you know they get scared and think they have it themselves. Then they go to bed, and send for the doctor. The doctor! All poppycock."

"Well, but Clare dear, if you were in charge of them, what would you do instead?"

"Cheer 'em up, that's the way to cure 'em."

"How would you cheer them up, darling?" Mother asked doubtfully.

"I? I'd tell 'em, '*Bah!*'"

# STATEMENT OF ARTHUR JAMES WENTWORTH, BACHELOR OF ARTS by Humphrey F. Ellis

My name is Arthur James Wentworth, I am unmarried and I am by profession an assistant master at Burgrove Preparatory School, Wilminster. The Headmaster is the Reverend Gregory Saunders, M.A. He is known to the boys as the Squid—not necessarily, I think, a term of opprobrium. He is a classical scholar of moderate attainments, a generous employer and much given to the use of the expression "The School must come first, Wentworth." I attach no particular meaning to this remark.

At 11:15 on the morning of Saturday, 8th July, I entered Classroom 4 for the purpose of instructing Set IIIA in Algebra. There were present Anderson, Atkins, Clarke, Etheridge, Hillman, Hopgood II, Mason, Otterway, Sapoulos, Trench and Williamson. Heathcote, who has, I am told, a boil, was absent. It should be explained that though I have given these names in the alphabetical order in which they appear in the school list, that is not the order in which the boys were sitting on this occasion. It is the custom at Burgrove for boys to sit according to their position in the previous week's

mark-lists. Thus in the front row were seated Etheridge, a most promising mathematician, Hillman,
Mason, Otterway and Clarke. Hopgood II, the boy
whom I am now accused of assaulting, was in the middle
of the second row. The third and last row was shared
by Sapoulos, a Greek, and Atkins, a cretin. I do not
think these facts have any bearing on anything that is
to follow, but I give them for the sake of completeness.

"This morning," I remarked, taking up my Hall and
Knight, "we will do problems," and I told them at once
that if there was any more of that groaning they would
do nothing but problems for the next month. It is my
experience, as an assistant-master of some years' standing, that if groaning is not checked immediately it may
swell to enormous proportions. I make it my business
to stamp on it.

Mason, a fair-haired boy with glasses, remarked when
the groaning had died down that it would not be possible to do problems for the next month, and on being
asked why not, replied that there were only three weeks
more of term. This was true, and I decided to make no
reply. He then asked if he could have a mark for that.
I said, "No, Mason, you may not," and, taking up my
book and a piece of chalk, read out, "I am just half as
old as my father and in twenty years I shall be five
years older than he was twenty years ago. How old
am I?" Atkins promptly replied, "Forty-two." I inquired of him how, unless he was gifted with super-
natural powers, he imagined he could produce the
answer without troubling to do any working-out. He
said, "I saw it in the *Schools Year-book*." This stupid

reply caused a great deal of laughter, which I suppressed.

I should have spoken sharply to Atkins, but at this moment I noticed that his neighbor Sapoulos, the Greek boy, appeared to be eating toffee, a practice which is forbidden at Burgrove during school hours. I ordered him to stand up. "Sapoulos," I said, "you are not perhaps quite used yet to our English ways, and I shall not punish you this time for your disobedience; but please understand that I will not have eating in my class. You did not come here to eat but to learn. If you try hard and pay attention I do not altogether despair of teaching you something, but if you do not wish to learn I cannot help you. You might as well go back to your own country." Mason, without being given permission to speak, cried excitedly, "He can't, sir. Didn't you know? His father was chased out of Greece in a revolution or something. A big man with a black beard chased him for three miles and he had to escape in a small boat. It's true, sir. You ask him. Sapoulos got hit on the knee with a brick, didn't you, Sappy? And his grandmother —at least I think it was his grandmother—"

"That will do, Mason," I said. "Who threw that?"

I am not, I hope, a martinet, but I will not tolerate the throwing of paper darts or other missiles in my algebra set. Some of the boys make small pellets out of their blotting paper and flick them with their garters. This sort of thing has to be put down with a firm hand or work becomes impossible. I accordingly warned the boy responsible that another offence would mean an imposition. He had the impertinence to ask what sort of an imposition. I said that it would be a pretty stiff imposition, and if he wished to know more exact details he had only to throw another dart to find out. He thereupon threw another dart.

I confess that at this I lost patience and threatened to keep the whole set in during the afternoon if I had any more trouble. The lesson then proceeded.

It was not until I had completed my working out of the problem on the board that I realised I had worked on the assumption—of course ridiculous—that I was *twice* my father's age instead of *half*. This gave the false figure of minus ninety for my own age. Some boy said "Crikey!" I at once whipped round and demanded to know who had spoken. Otterway suggested that it might have been Hopgood II talking in his sleep. I was about to reprimand Otterway for impertinence when I realised that Hopgood actually was asleep and had in fact, according to Williamson, been asleep since the beginning of the period. Mason said, "He hasn't missed much anyway."

I then threw my Hall and Knight. It has been suggested that it was intended to hit Hopgood II. This is false. I never wake up sleeping boys by throwing books at them, as hundreds of old Burgrove boys will be able to testify. I intended to hit Mason, and it was by a mischance which I shall always regret that Hopgood was struck. I have had, as I told my Headmaster, a great deal to put up with from Mason, and no one who knows the boy blames me for the attempt to do him some physical violence. It is indeed an accepted maxim in the Common Room that physical violence is the only method of dealing with Mason which produces any results; to this the Headmaster some time ago added a rider that the boy be instructed to remove his spectacles before being assaulted. That I forgot to do this must be put down to the natural agitation of a mathematics master caught out in an error. But I blame myself for it.

I do not blame myself for the unfortunate stunning of Hopgood II. It was an accident. I did all I could for the boy when it was discovered (I think by Etheridge) that he had been rendered unconscious. I immediately summoned the Headmaster and we talked the matter over. We agreed that concealment was impossible and that I must give a full account of the circumstances to the police. Meanwhile the work of the school was to go on as usual; Hopgood himself would have wished it. The Headmaster added that in any case the School must come first.

I have made this statement after being duly cautioned, of my own free will and in the presence of witnesses. I have read it through three times with considerable satisfaction, and am prepared to state on oath that it is a true and full account of the circumstances leading up to the accident to Hopgood II. I wish only to add that the boy is now none the worse for the blow, and has indeed shown increased zeal for his studies since the occurrence.

(Signed) A. J. WENTWORTH, B.A.
8th July, 1939

## THE BURGLARS by Kenneth Grahame

It was much too fine a night to think of going to bed at once, and so, although the witching hour of nine P.M. had struck, Edward and I were still leaning out of the open window in our nightshirts, watching the play of the cedar-branch shadows on the moonlit lawn, and planning schemes of fresh devilry for the sunshiny morrow. From below, strains of the jocund piano declared that the Olympians were enjoying themselves in their listless, impotent way; for the new curate had been bidden to dinner that night, and was at the moment unclerically proclaiming to all the world that he feared no foe. His discordant vociferations doubtless started a train of thought in Edward's mind, for the youth presently remarked, *à propos* of nothing that had been said before, "I believe the new curate's rather gone on Aunt Maria."

I scouted the notion. "Why, she's quite old," I said. (She must have seen some five-and-twenty summers.)

"Of course she is," replied Edward, scornfully. "It's not her, it's her money he's after, you bet!"

"Didn't know she had any money," I observed timidly.

"Sure to have," said my brother, with confidence. "Heaps and heaps."

Silence ensued, both our minds being busy with the new situation thus presented,—mine, in wonderment at this flaw that so often declared itself in enviable natures of fullest endowment,—in a grown-up man and a good cricketer, for instance, even as this curate; Edward's (apparently), in the consideration of how such a state of things, supposing it existed, could be best turned to his own advantage.

"Bobby Ferris told me," began Edward in due course, "that there was a fellow spooning his sister once—"

"What's spooning?" I asked meekly.

"Oh, *I* dunno," said Edward, indifferently. "It's—it's —it's just a thing they do, you know. And he used to carry notes and messages and things between 'em, and he got a shilling almost every time."

"What, from each of 'em?" I innocently inquired.

Edward looked at me with scornful pity. "Girls never have any money," he briefly explained. "But she did his exercises and got him out of rows, and told stories for him when he needed it—and much better ones than he could have made up for himself. Girls are useful in some ways. So he was living in clover, when unfortunately they went and quarreled about something."

"Don't see what that's got to do with it," I said.

"Nor don't I," rejoined Edward. "But anyhow the notes and things stopped, and so did the shillings. Bobby was fairly cornered, for he had bought two ferrets on tick, and promised to pay a shilling a week, thinking the shillings were going on for ever, the silly young ass. So when the week was up, and he was being dunned for the shilling, he went off to the fellow and said, 'Your broken-hearted Bella implores you to meet her at sundown,—by the hollow oak, as of old, be it only for a moment. Do not fail!' He got all that out of some rotten book, of course. The fellow looked puzzled and said,—

" 'What hollow oak? I don't know any hollow oak.'

" 'Perhaps it was the Royal Oak?' said Bobby promptly, 'cos he saw he had made a slip, through trusting too much to the rotten book; but this didn't seem to make the fellow any happier."

"Should think not," I said, "the Royal Oak's an awful low sort of pub."

"I know," said Edward. "Well, at last the fellow said, 'I think I know what she means: the hollow tree in your father's paddock. It happens to be an elm, but she wouldn't know the difference. All right: say I'll be there.' Bobby hung about a bit, for he hadn't got his money. 'She was crying awfully,' he said. Then he got his shilling."

"And wasn't the fellow riled," I inquired, "when he got to the place and found nothing?"

"He found Bobby," said Edward, indignantly. "Young Ferris was a gentleman, every inch of him. He brought the fellow another message from Bella: 'I dare not leave the house. My cruel parents immure me closely. If you only knew what I suffer. Your broken-hearted Bella.' Out of the same rotten book. This made the fellow a little suspicious, 'cos it was the old Ferrises who had been keen about the thing all through: the fellow, you see, had tin."

"But what's that got to—" I began again.

"Oh, *I* dunno," said Edward, impatiently. "I'm telling you just what Bobby told me. He got suspicious, anyhow, but he couldn't exactly call Bella's brother a liar, so Bobby escaped for the time. But when he was in a hole next week, over a stiff French exercise, and tried the same sort of game on his sister, she was too sharp for him, and he got caught out. Somehow women seem more mistrustful than men. They're so beastly suspicious by nature, you know."

"*I* know," said I. "But did the two—the fellow and the sister—make it up afterwards?"

"I don't remember about that," replied Edward, indifferently; "but Bobby got packed off to school a whole year earlier than his people meant to send him,—which was just what he wanted. So you see it all came right in the end!"

I was trying to puzzle out the moral of this story—it was evidently meant to contain one somewhere—when a flood of golden lamplight mingled with the moon-rays on the lawn, and Aunt Maria and the new curate strolled out on the grass below us, and took the direction of a garden-seat that was backed by a dense laurel shrubbery reaching round in a half-circle to the house. Edward meditated moodily. "If we only knew what they were talking about," said he, "you'd soon see whether I was right or not. Look here! Let's send the kid down by the porch to reconnoitre!"

"Harold's asleep," I said; "it seems rather a shame—"

"Oh, rot!" said my brother; "he's the youngest, and he's got to do as he's told!"

So the luckless Harold was hauled out of bed and given his sailing-orders. He was naturally rather vexed at being stood up suddenly on the cold floor, and the job had no particular interest for him; but he was both staunch and well disciplined. The means of exit were simple enough. A porch of iron trellis came up to within easy reach of the window, and was habitually used by all three of us, when modestly anxious to avoid public notice. Harold climbed deftly down the porch like a white rat, and his night-gown glimmered a moment on the gravel walk ere he was lost to sight in the darkness of the shrubbery. A brief interval of silence ensued, broken suddenly by a sound of scuffle, and then a shrill, long-drawn squeal, as of metallic surfaces in friction. Our scout had fallen into the hands of the enemy!

Indolence alone had made us devolve the task of investigation on our younger brother. Now that danger had declared itself, there was no hesitation. In a second we were down the side of the porch, and crawling Cherokee-wise through the laurels to the back of the garden-seat. Piteous was the sight that greeted us. Aunt Maria was on the seat, in a white evening frock, looking—for an aunt—really quite nice. On the lawn stood an incensed curate, grasping our small brother by a large ear, which—judging from the row he was making —seemed on the point of parting company with the head it adorned. The gruesome noise he was emitting did not really affect us otherwise than æsthetically. To one who has tried both, the wail of genuine physical anguish is easy distinguishable from the pumped-up *ad misericordiam* blubber. Harold's could clearly be recognised as belonging to the latter class. "Now, you young—" (whelp, *I* think it was, but Edward stoutly maintains it was devil), said the curate, sternly; "tell us what you mean by it!"

"Well, leggo of my ear then!" shrilled Harold, "and I'll tell you the solemn truth!"

"Very well," agreed the curate, releasing him; "now go ahead, and don't lie more than you can help."

We abode the promised disclosure without the least misgiving; but even we had hardly given Harold due credit for his fertility of resource and powers of imagination.

"I had just finished saying my prayers," began that young gentleman, slowly, "when I happened to look out of the window, and on the lawn I saw a sight which froze the marrow in my veins! A burglar was approaching the house with snake-like tread! He had a scowl and a dark lantern, and he was armed to the teeth!"

We listened with interest. The style, though unlike Harold's native notes, seemed strangely familiar.

"Go on," said the curate, grimly.

"Pausing in his stealthy career," continued Harold, "he gave a low whistle. Instantly the signal was responded to, and from the adjacent shadows two more figures glided forth. The miscreants were both armed to the teeth."

"Excellent," said the curate; "proceed."

"The robber chief," pursued Harold, warming to his

work, "joined his nefarious comrades, and conversed with them in silent tones. His expression was truly ferocious, and I ought to have said that he was armed to the t—"

"There, never mind his teeth," interrupted the curate, rudely; "there's too much jaw about you altogether. Hurry up and have done."

"I was in a frightful funk," continued the narrator, warily guarding his ear with his hand, "but just then the drawing-room window opened, and you and Aunt Maria came out—I mean emerged. The burglars vanished silently into the laurels, with horrid implications!"

The curate looked slightly puzzled. The tale was well sustained, and certainly circumstantial. After all, the boy might have really seen something. How was the poor man to know—though the chaste and lofty diction might have supplied a hint—that the whole yarn was a free adaptation from the last Penny Dreadful lent us by the knife-and-boot boy?

"Why did you not alarm the house?" he asked.

" 'Cos I was afraid," said Harold, sweetly, "that p'raps they mightn't believe me!"

"But how did you get down here, you naughty little boy?" put in Aunt Maria.

Harold was hard pressed—by his own flesh and blood, too!

At that moment Edward touched me on the shoulder and glided off through the laurels. When some ten yards away he gave a low whistle. I replied by another. The effect was magical. Aunt Maria started up with a shriek. Harold gave one startled glance around, and then fled like a hare, made straight for the back door, burst in upon the servants at supper, and buried himself in the broad bosom of the cook, his special ally. The curate faced the laurels—hesitatingly. But Aunt Maria flung herself on him. "O Mr. Hodgitts!" I heard her cry, "you are brave! for my sake do not be rash!" He was not rash. When I peeped out a second later, the coast was entirely clear.

By this time there were sounds of a household timidly emerging; and Edward remarked to me that perhaps we had better be off. Retreat was an easy matter. A stunted laurel gave a leg up on to the garden wall, which led in its turn to the roof of an out-house, up which, at a dubious angle, we could crawl to the window of the box-room. This overland route had been revealed to us one day by the domestic cat, when hard pressed in the course of an otter-hunt, in which the cat—somewhat unwillingly—was filling the title *rôle;* and it had proved distinctly useful on occasions like the present. We were snug in bed—minus some cuticle from knees and elbows —and Harold, sleepily chewing something sticky, had been carried up in the arms of the friendly cook, ere the clamour of the burglar-hunters had died away.

The curate's undaunted demeanour, as reported by Aunt Maria, was generally supposed to have terrified the burglars into flight, and much kudos accrued to him thereby. Some days later, however, when he had dropped in to afternoon tea, and was making a mild curatorial joke about the moral courage required for taking the last piece of bread-and-butter, I felt con-strained to remark dreamily, and as it were to the

universe at large, "Mr. Hodgitts! you are brave! for my
sake, do not be rash!"

Fortunately for me, the vicar was also a caller on that
day; and it was always a comparatively easy matter to
dodge my long-coated friend in the open.

THE PETERKINS

# AGAMEMNON'S CAREER  by Lucretia P. Hale

THERE had apparently been some mistake in Agamemnon's education. He had been to a number of colleges, indeed, but he had never completed his course in any one. He had continually fallen into some difficulty with the authorities. It was singular, for he was of an inquiring mind, and had always tried to find out what would be expected of him, but had never hit upon the right thing.

Solomon John thought the trouble might be in what they called the elective system, where you were to choose what study you might take. This had always bewildered Agamemnon a good deal.

"And how was a feller to tell," Solomon John had asked, "whether he wanted to study a thing before he tried it? It might turn out awful hard!"

Agamemnon had always been fond of reading, from his childhood up. He was at his book all day long. Mrs. Peterkin had imagined he would come out a great scholar, because she could never get him away from his books.

And so it was in his colleges; he was always to be found in the library, reading and reading. But they were always the wrong books.

For instance: the class were required to prepare themselves on the Spartan war. This turned Agamemnon's attention to the Fenians, and to study the subject he read up on "Charles O'Malley," and "Harry Lorrequer," and some later novels of that sort, which did not help him on the subject required, yet took up all his time, so that he found himself unfitted for anything else when the examinations came. In consequence he was requested to leave.

Agamemnon always missed in his recitations, for the same reason that Elizabeth Eliza did not get on in school, because he was always asked the questions he did not know. It seemed provoking; if the professors had only asked something else! But they always hit upon the very things he had not studied up.

Mrs. Peterkin felt this was encouraging, for Agamemnon knew the things they did not know in colleges. In colleges they were willing to take for students only those who already knew certain things. She thought Agamemnon might be a professor in a college for those students who didn't know those things.

"I suppose these professors could not have known a great deal," she added, "or they would not have asked you so many questions; they would have told you something."

Agamemnon had left another college on account of a mistake he had made with some of his classmates. They had taken a great deal of trouble to bring some wood from a distant wood-pile to make a bonfire with, under one of the professors' windows. Agamemnon had felt it would be a compliment to the professor.

It was with bonfires that heroes had been greeted on their return from successful wars. In this way beacon-lights had been kindled upon lofty heights, that had inspired mariners seeking their home after distant adventures. As he plodded back and forward he imagined himself some hero of antiquity. He was reading "Plutarch's Lives" with deep interest. This had been recommended at a former college, and he was now taking it up in the midst of his French course. He fancied, even, that some future Plutarch was growing up in Lynn, perhaps, who would write of this night of suffering, and glorify its heroes.

For himself he took a severe cold and suffered from chilblains, in consequence of going back and forward through the snow, carrying the wood.

But the flames of the bonfire caught the blinds of the professor's room, and set fire to the building, and came near burning up the whole institution. Agamemnon regretted the result as much as his predecessor, who gave him his name, must have regretted that other bonfire, on the shores of Aulis, that deprived him of a daughter.

The result for Agamemnon was that he was requested to leave, after having been in the institution but a few months.

He left another college in consequence of a misunderstanding about the hour for morning prayers. He went every day regularly at ten o'clock, but found, afterward, that he should have gone at half-past six. This hour seemed to him and to Mrs. Peterkin unseasonable, at a time of year when the sun was not up, and he would have been obliged to go to the expense of candles.

Agamemnon was always willing to try another college, wherever he could be admitted. He wanted to attain knowledge, however it might be found. But, after going to five, and leaving each before the year was out, he gave it up.

He determined to lay out the money that would have been expended in a collegiate education in buying an Encyclopaedia, the most complete that he could find, and to spend his life studying it systematically. He would not content himself with merely reading it, but he would study into each subject as it came up, and perfect himself in that subject. By the time, then, that he had finished the Encyclopaedia he should have embraced all knowledge, and have experienced much of it.

The family were much interested in this plan of making practice of every subject that came up.

He did not, of course, get on very fast in this way. In the second column of the very first page he met with A as a note in music. This led him to the study of music. He bought a flute, and took some lessons, and attempted to accompany Elizabeth Eliza on the piano. This, of course, distracted him from his work on the Encyclopaedia. But he did not wish to return to A until he felt perfect in music. This required a long time.

Then in this same paragraph a reference was made; in it he was requested to "see Keys." It was necessary, then, to turn to "Keys." This was about the time the family were moving, which we have mentioned, when the difficult subject of keys came up, that suggested to him his own simple invention, and the hope of getting a patent for it. This led him astray, as inventions before have done with master-minds, so that he was drawn aside from his regular study.

The family, however, were perfectly satisfied with the career Agamemnon had chosen. It would help them all, in any path of life, if he should master the Encyclopaedia in a thorough way.

Mr. Peterkin agreed it would in the end be not as expensive as a college course, even if Agamemnon should buy all the different Encyclopaedias that appeared. There would be no "spreads" involved; no expense of receiving friends at entertainments in college; he could live at home, so that it would not be necessary to fit up another room, as at college. At all the times of his leaving he had sold out favorably to other occupants.

Solomon John's destiny was more uncertain. He was looking forward to being a doctor some time, but he had not decided whether to be allopathic or homoeopathic, or whether he could not better invent his own pills. And he could not understand how to obtain his doctor's degree.

For a few weeks he acted as clerk in a druggist's store. But he could serve only in the tooth-brush and soap department, because it was found he was not familiar enough with the Latin language to compound the drugs. He agreed to spend his evenings in studying the Latin grammar; but his course was interrupted by his being dismissed for treating the little boys too frequently to soda.

The little boys were going through the schools regularly. The family had been much exercised with regard to their education. Elizabeth Eliza felt that everything should be expected from them; they ought to take advantage from the family mistakes. Every new method that came up was tried upon the little boys. They had been taught spelling by all the different systems, and were just able to read, when Mr. Peterkin learned that it was now considered best that children should not be taught to read till they were ten years old.

Mrs. Peterkin was in despair. Perhaps, if their books were taken from them even then, they might forget what they had learned. But no, the evil was done; the brain had received certain impressions that could not be blurred over.

This was long ago, however. The little boys had since entered the public schools. They went also to a gymnasium, and a whittling school, and joined a class in music, and another in dancing; they went to some afternoon lectures for children, when there was no other school, and belonged to a walking-club. Still Mr. Peterkin was dissatisfied by the slowness of their progress. He visited the schools himself, and found that they did not lead their classes. It seemed to him a great deal of time was spent in things that were not instructive, such as putting on and taking off their india-rubber boots.

Elizabeth Eliza proposed that they should be taken from school and taught by Agamemnon from the Encyclopaedia. The rest of the family might help in the education at all hours of the day. Solomon John could take up the Latin grammar; and she could give lessons in French.

The little boys were enchanted with the plan, only they did not want to have the study-hours all the time.

Mr. Peterkin, however, had a magnificent idea, that they should make their life one grand Object Lesson. They should begin at breakfast, and study everything put upon the table,—the material of which it was made, and where it came from. In the study of the letter A, Agamemnon had embraced the study of music, and from one meal they might gain instruction enough for a day.

"We shall have the assistance," said Mr. Peterkin, "of Agamemnon, with his Encyclopaedia."

Agamemnon modestly suggested that he had not yet got out of A, and in their first breakfast everything would therefore have to begin with A.

"That would not be impossible," said Mr. Peterkin. "There is Amanda, who will wait on table, to start with"—

"We could have 'am-and-eggs," suggested Solomon John.

Mrs. Peterkin was distressed. It was hard enough to think of anything for breakfast, and impossible if it all had to begin with one letter.

Elizabeth Eliza thought it would not be necessary. All they were to do was to ask questions, as in examination papers, and find their answers as they could. They could still apply to the Encyclopaedia, even if it were not in Agamemnon's alphabetical course.

Mr. Peterkin suggested a great variety. One day they would study the botany of the breakfast-table; another day, its natural history. The study of butter would include that of the cow. Even that of the butter-dish would bring in geology. The little boys were charmed at the idea of learning pottery from the cream-jug, and they were promised a potter's wheel directly.

"You see, my dear," said Mr. Peterkin to his wife, "before many weeks we shall be drinking our milk from jugs made by our children."

Elizabeth Eliza hoped for a thorough study.

"Yes," said Mr. Peterkin, "we might begin with botany. That would be near to Agamemnon alphabetically. We ought to find out the botany of butter. On what does the cow feed?"

The little boys were eager to go out and see.

"If she eats clover," said Mr. Peterkin, "we shall expect the botany of clover."

The little boys insisted that they were to begin the next day; that very evening they should go out and study the cow.

Mrs. Peterkin sighed, and decided she would order a simple breakfast. The little boys took their note-books and pencils, and clambered upon the fence, where they seated themselves in a row.

For there were three little boys. So it was now supposed. They were always coming in or going out, and it had been difficult to count them, and nobody was very sure how many there were.

There they sat, however, on the fence, looking at the cow. She looked at them with large eyes.

"She won't eat," they cried, "while we are looking at her!"

So they turned about, and pretended to look into the street, and seated themselves that way, turning their heads back, from time to time, to see the cow.

"Now she is nibbling a clover."

"No, that is a bit of sorrel."

"It's a whole handful of grass."

"What kind of grass?" they exclaimed.

It was very hard, sitting with their backs to the cow, and pretending to the cow that they were looking into the street, and yet to be looking at the cow all the time, and finding out what she was eating; and the upper rail of the fence was narrow and a little sharp. It was very high, too, for some additional rails had been put on to prevent the cow from jumping into the garden or street.

Suddenly, looking out into the hazy twilight, Elizabeth Eliza saw six legs and six india-rubber boots in the air, and the little boys disappeared!

"They are tossed by the cow! The little boys are tossed by the cow!"

Mrs. Peterkin rushed for the window, but fainted on the way. Solomon John and Elizabeth Eliza were hurrying to the door, but stopped, not knowing what to do next. Mrs. Peterkin recovered herself with a supreme effort, and sent them out to the rescue.

But what could they do? The fence had been made so high, to keep the cow out, that nobody could get in. The boy that did the milking had gone off with the key of the outer gate, and perhaps with the key of the shed door. Even if that were not locked, before

Agamemnon could get round by the wood-shed and cow-shed, the little boys might be gored through and through!

Elizabeth Eliza ran to the neighbors, Solomon John to the druggist's for plasters, while Agamemnon made his way through the dining-room to the wood-shed and outer-shed door. Mr. Peterkin mounted the outside of the fence, while Mrs. Peterkin begged him not to put himself in danger. He climbed high enough to view the scene. He held to the corner post and reported what he saw.

They were not gored. The cow was at the other end of the lot. One of the little boys was lying in a bunch of dark leaves. He was moving.

The cow glared, but did not stir. Another little boy was pulling his india-rubber boots out of the mud. The cow still looked at him.

Another was feeling the top of his head. The cow began to crop the grass, still looking at him.

Agamemnon had reached and opened the shed-door. The little boys were next seen running toward it.

A crowd of neighbors, with pitchforks, had returned meanwhile with Elizabeth Eliza. Solomon John had brought four druggists. But, by the time they had reached the house, the three little boys were safe in the arms of their mother!

"This is too dangerous a form of education," she cried; "I had rather they went to school."

"No!" they bravely cried. They were still willing to try the other way.

## THREE MEN IN A BOAT (Chapter VI) by Jerome K. Jerome

It was a glorious morning, late spring or early summer, as you care to take it, when the dainty sheen of grass and leaf is blushing to a deeper green; and the year seems like a fair young maid, trembling with strange, wakening pulses on the brink of womanhood.

The quaint back streets of Kingston, where they came down to the water's edge, looked quite picturesque in the flashing sunlight, the glinting river with its drifting barges, the wooded towpath, the trim-kept villas on the other side, Harris, in a red and orange blazer, grunting away at the sculls, the distant glimpses of the gray old palace of the Tudors, all made a sunny picture, so bright but calm, so full of life, and yet so peaceful, that, early in the day though it was, I felt myself being dreamily lulled off into a musing fit.

I mused on Kingston, or "Kyningestun," as it was once called in the days when Saxon "kinges" were crowned there. Great Cæsar crossed the river there, and the Roman legions camped upon its sloping uplands. Cæsar, like, in later years, Elizabeth, seems to have stopped everywhere; only he was more respectable than good Queen Bess; he didn't put up at the public-houses.

She was nuts on public-houses, was England's virgin queen. There's scarcely a pub, of any attractions within ten miles of London that she does not seem to have looked in at, or stopped at, or slept at, some time or other. I wonder now, supposing Harris, say, turned over a new leaf, and became a great and good man, and got to be prime minister, and died, if they would put up signs over the public-houses that he had patronized: "Harris had a glass of bitter in this house;" "Harris had two of Scotch cold here in the summer of '88;" "Harris was chucked from here in December, 1886."

No, there would be too many of them! It would be the houses that he had never entered that would become famous. "Only house in South London that Harris never had a drink in!" The people would flock to it to see what could have been the matter with it.

How poor weak-minded King Edwy must have hated Kyningestun! The coronation feast had been too much for him. Maybe boar's head stuffed with sugar-plums did not agree with him (it wouldn't with me, I know), and he had had enough of sack and mead; so he slipped from the noisy revel to steal a quiet moonlight hour with his beloved Elgiva.

Perhaps, from the casement, standing hand in hand, they were watching the calm moonlight on the river, while from the distant halls the boisterous revelry floated in broken bursts of faint-heard din and tumult.

Then brutal Odo and St. Dunstan force their rude way into the quiet room, and hurl coarse insults at the sweet-faced queen, and drag poor Edwy back to the loud clamor of the drunken brawl.

Years later, to the crash of battle-music, Saxon kings and Saxon revelry were buried side by side, and Kingston's greatness passed away for a time, to rise once more when Hampton Court became a palace of the Tudors and the Stuarts, and the royal barges strained at their moorings on the river's bank, and bright-cloaked gallants swaggered down the water-steps to cry: "What ferry, ho! Gadzooks, gramercy!"

Many of the old houses round about speak very plainly of those days when Kingston was a royal borough, and nobles and courtiers lived there, near their king, and the long road to the palace gates was gay all day with clanking steel and prancing palfreys, and rustling silks and velvets, and fair faces. The large and spacious houses, with their oriel, latticed windows, their huge fireplaces, and their gabled roofs, breathe of the days of hose and doublet, of pearl-embroidered stomachers, and complicated oaths. They were upraised in the days "when men knew how to build." The hard red bricks have only grown more firmly set with time, and their oak stairs do not creak and grunt when you try to go down them quietly.

Speaking of oak staircases reminds me that there is a magnificent carved oak staircase in one of the houses in Kingston. It is a shop now, in the market-place, but it was evidently once the mansion of some great personage. A friend of mine, who lives at Kingston, went in there to buy a hat one day, and, in a thoughtless moment, put his hand in his pocket and paid for it then and there.

The shopman (he knows my friend) was naturally a little staggered at first; but quickly recovering himself, and feeling that something ought to be done to encourage this sort of thing, asked our hero if he would like to see some fine old carved oak. My friend said he would; and the shopman thereupon took him through the shop, and up the staircase of the house. The balusters were a superb piece of workmanship, and the wall all the way up was oak-paneled, with carving that would have done credit to a palace. From the stairs they went into the drawing-room, which was a large, bright room, decorated with a somewhat startling though cheerful paper of a blue ground. There was nothing, however, remarkable about the apartment, and my friend wondered why he had been brought there. The proprietor went up to the paper, and tapped it. It gave forth a wooden sound.

"Oak," he explained. "All carved oak, right up to the ceiling, just the same as you saw on the staircase."

"But, great Cæsar! man," expostulated my friend; "you don't mean to say you have covered over oak with blue wall-paper?"

"Yes," was the reply; "it was expensive work. Had to match-board it all over first, of course. But the room looks cheerful now. It was awful gloomy before."

I can't say I altogether blame the man (which is doubtless a great relief to his mind). From his point of view, which would be that of the average householder, desiring to take life as lightly as possible, and not that of the old curiosity-shop maniac, there is reason on his side. Carved oak is very pleasant to look at, and to have a little of, but it is no doubt somewhat depressing to live in, for those whose fancy does not lie that way. It would be like living in a church.

No, what was sad in his case was that he, who didn't care for carved oak, should have his drawing-room paneled with it, while people who do care for it have to pay enormous prices to get it. It seems to be the rule of this world. Each person has what he doesn't want, and other people have what he does want.

Married men have wives, and don't seem to want them; and young single fellows cry out that they can't get them. Poor people who can hardly keep themselves have eight hearty children. Rich old couples, with no one to leave their money to, die childless.

Then there are girls with lovers. The girls that have lovers never want them. They say they would rather be without them, that they bother them, and why don't they go and make love to Miss Smith and Miss Brown, who are plain and elderly, and haven't got any lovers? They themselves don't want lovers. They never mean to marry.

It does not do to dwell on these things; it makes one so sad.

There was a boy at our school, we used to call him Sandford and Merton. His real name was Stivvings. He was the most extraordinary lad I ever came across. I believe he really liked study. He used to get into awful rows for sitting up in bed and reading Greek; and as for French irregular verbs there was simply no keeping him away from them. He was full of weird and unnatural notions about being a credit to his parents and an honor to the school; and he yearned to win prizes, and grow up and be a clever man, and had all those sorts of weak-minded ideas. I never knew such a strange creature, yet harmless, mind you, as the babe unborn.

Well, that boy used to get ill about twice a week, so that he couldn't go to school. There never was such a boy to get ill as that Sandford and Merton. If there was any known disease going within ten miles of him, he had it, and had it badly. He would take bronchitis in the dog-days, and have hay-fever at Christmas. After a six weeks' period of drought, he would be stricken down with rheumatic fever; and he would go out in a November fog and come home with a sunstroke.

They put him under laughing-gas one year, poor lad, and drew all his teeth, and gave him a false set, because he suffered so terribly with toothache; and then it turned to neuralgia and earache. He was never without a cold, except once for nine weeks while he had scarlet fever; and he always had chilblains. During the great cholera scare of 1871, our neighborhood was singularly free from it. There was only one reputed case in the whole parish: that case was young Stivvings.

He had to stop in bed when he was ill, and eat chicken and custards and hot-house grapes; and he would lie there and sob, because they wouldn't let him do Latin exercises, and took his German grammar away from him.

And we other boys, who would have sacrificed ten

terms of our school life for the sake of being ill for a day, and had no desire whatever to give our parents any excuse for being stuck-up about us, couldn't catch so much as a stiff neck. We fooled about in draughts, and it did us good, and freshened us up; and we took things to make us sick, and they made us fat, and gave us an appetite. Nothing we could think of seemed to make us ill until the holidays began. Then, on the breaking-up day, we caught colds, and whooping-cough, and all kinds of disorders, which lasted till the term recommenced; when, in spite of everything we could maneuver to the contrary, we would get suddenly well again and be better than ever.

Such is life; and we are but as grass that is cut down, and put into the oven and baked.

To go back to the carved-oak question, they must have had very fair notions of the artistic and the beautiful, our great-great-grandfathers. Why, all our art treasures of to-day are only the dug-up commonplaces of three or four hundred years ago. I wonder if there is real intrinsic beauty in the old soup-plates, beer-mugs, and candle-snuffers that we prize so now, or if it is only the halo of age glowing around them that gives them their charms in our eyes. The "old blue" that we hang about our walls as ornaments were the common everyday household utensils of a few centuries ago; and the pink shepherds and the yellow shepherdesses that we hang round now for all our friends to gush over, and pretend they understand, were the unvalued mantel ornaments that the mother of the eighteenth century would have given the baby to suck when he cried.

Will it be the same in the future? Will the prized treasures of to-day always be the cheap trifles of the day before? Will rows of our willow-pattern dinner-plates be ranged above the chimney-pieces of the great in the years 2000 and odd? Will the white cups with the gold rim and the beautiful gold flower inside (species unknown), that our Sarah Janes now break in sheer light-heartedness of spirit, be carefully mended, and stood upon a bracket, and dusted only by the lady of the house?

That china dog that ornaments the bedroom of my furnished lodgings. It is a white dog. Its eyes are blue. Its nose is a delicate red, with black spots. Its head is painfully erect, and its expression is amiability carried to the verge of imbecility. I do not admire it myself. Considered as a work of art, I may say it irritates me. Thoughtless friends jeer at it, and even my landlady herself has no admiration for it, and excuses its presence by the circumstance that her aunt gave it to her.

But in two hundred years' time it is more than prob-able that that dog will be dug up from some where or other, minus its legs, and with its tail broken, and will be sold for old china, and put in a glass cabinet. And people will pass it round, and admire it. They will be struck by the wonderful depth of the color on the nose, and speculate as to how beautiful the bit of the tail that is lost no doubt was.

We, in this age, do not see the beauty of that dog. We are too familiar with it. It is like the sunset and the stars: we are not awed by their loveliness because they are common to our eyes. So it is with that china dog. In 2288 people will gush over it. The making of such dogs will have become lost art. Our descendants will wonder how we did it, and say how clever we were. We shall be referred to lovingly as "those grand old artists that flourished in the nineteenth century, and produced those china dogs."

The "sampler" that the oldest daughter did at school will be spoken of as "tapestry of the Victorian era," and be also priceless. The blue-and-white mugs of the present day road-side inn will be hunted up, all cracked and chipped, and sold for their weight in gold, and rich people will use them for claret cups; and travelers from Japan will buy up all the "Presents from Ramsgate," and "Souvenirs of Margate," that may have escaped destruction, and take them back to Jedo as ancient English curios.

At this point Harris threw away the sculls, got up and left his seat, and sat on his back, and stuck his legs in the air. Montmorency howled, and turned a somersault, and the top hamper jumped up, and all the things came out.

I was somewhat surprised, but I did not lose my temper. I said, pleasantly enough:

"Halloo! what's that for?"

"What's that for? Why——"

No, on second thought, I will not repeat what Harris said. I may have been to blame, I admit it; but nothing excuses violence of language and coarseness of expression, especially in a man who has been carefully brought up, as I know Harris has been. I was thinking of other things, and forgot, as any one might easily understand, that I was steering, and the consequence was that we had got mixed up a good deal with the tow-path. It was difficult to say, for the moment, which was us and which was the Middlesex bank of the river; but we found out after a while, and separated ourselves.

Harris, however, said he had done enough for a bit, and proposed that I should take a turn; so, as we were in, I got out and took the tow-line, and ran the boat on past Hampton Court. What a dear old wall that is that runs along by the river there! I never pass it without feeling better for the sight of it. Such a mellow, bright, sweet old wall; what a charming picture it would make, with the lichen creeping here, and the moss growing there, a shy young vine peeping over the top at this spot, to see what is going on upon the busy river, and the sober old ivy clustering a little further down. There are fifty shades and tints and hues in every ten yards of that old wall. If I could only draw, and knew how to paint, I could make a lovely sketch of that old wall, I'm sure. I've often thought I should like to live at Hampton Court. It looks so peaceful and so quiet, and is such a dear old place to ramble round in the early morning before many people are about.

But there, I don't suppose I should really care for it when it came to actual practice. It would be so ghastly dull and depressing in the evening when your lamp cast uncanny shadows on the paneled walls, and the echo of distant feet rang through the cold stone corridors, and now drew nearer, and now died away, and all was deathlike silence, save the beating of one's own heart.

We are creatures of the sun, we men and women. We love light and life. That is why we crowd into the towns and cities, and the country grows more and more deserted every year. In the sunlight—in the daytime, when Nature is alive and busy all around us, we like the open hillsides and the deep woods well enough: but in the night, when our Mother Earth has gone to sleep, and left us waking, oh! the world seems so lonesome, and we get frightened, like children in a silent house. Then we sit and sob and long for the gas-lit streets, and the sound of human voices, and the answering throb of human life. We feel so helpless and so little in the great stillness, when the dark trees rustle in the night wind. There are so many ghosts about, and their silent sighs make us feel so sad. Let us gather together in the great cities, and light huge bonfires of a million gas-jets, and shout and sing together, and feel brave.

Harris asked me if I'd ever been in the maze at Hampton Court. He said he went in once to show somebody else the way. He had studied it up in a map, and it was so simple that it seemed foolish—hardly worth the twopence charged for admission. Harris said he thought that map must have been got up as a practical joke, because it wasn't a bit like the real thing, and only misleading. It was a country cousin that Harris took in. He said:

"We'll just go in there, so that you can say you've been, but it's very simple. It's absurd to call it a maze. You keep on taking the first turning to the right. We'll just walk round for ten minutes, and then go and get some lunch."

They met some people soon after they had got inside, who said they had been there for three-quarters of an hour, and had had about enough of it. Harris told them they could follow him, if they liked; he was just going in, and then should turn round and come out again. They said it was very kind of him, and fell behind and followed.

They picked up various other people who wanted to get it over, as they went along, until they had absorbed all the persons in the maze. People who had given up all hopes of ever getting either in or out, or of ever seeing their home and friends again, plucked up courage at the sight of Harris and his party, and joined the procession, blessing him. Harris said he should judge there must have been twenty people following him, in all; and one woman with a baby, who had been there all the morning, insisted on taking his arm, for fear of losing him.

Harris kept on turning to the right, but it seemed a long way, and his cousin said he supposed it was a very big maze.

"Oh, one of the largest in Europe," said Harris.

"Yes, it must be," replied the cousin, "because we've walked a good two miles already."

Harris began to think it rather strange himself, but he held on until, at last, they passed the half of a penny bun on the ground that Harris' cousin swore he had noticed there seven minutes ago. Harris said: "Oh, impossible!" but the woman with the baby said, "Not at all," as she herself had taken it from the child, and thrown it down there, just before she met Harris. She also added that she wished she never had met Harris, and expressed an opinion that he was an impostor. That made Harris mad, and he produced his map, and explained his theory.

"The map may be all right enough," said one of the party, "if you know whereabouts in it we are now."

Harris didn't know and suggested that the best thing to do would be to go back to the entrance, and begin again. For the beginning again part of it there was not much enthusiasm; but with regard to the advisability of going back to the entrance there was complete unanimity, and so they turned, and trailed after Harris again, in the opposite direction. About ten minutes more passed, and then they found themselves in the center.

Harris thought at first of pretending that that was what he had been aiming at; but the crowd looked dangerous, and he decided to treat it as an accident.

Anyhow, they had got something to start from then. They did know where they were, and the map was once more consulted, and the thing seemed simpler than ever, and off they started for the third time.

And three minutes later they were back in the center again.

After that they simply couldn't get anywhere else. Whatever way they turned brought them back to the middle. It became so regular at length, that some of the people stopped there, and waited for the others to take a walk round, and come back to them. Harris drew out his map again, after a while, but the sight of it only infuriated the mob, and they told him to go and curl his hair with it. Harris said that he couldn't help feeling that, to a certain extent, he had become un-popular.

They all got crazy at last, and sung out for the keeper, and the man came and climbed up the ladder outside, and shouted out directions to them. But all their heads were, by this time, in such a confused whirl that they were incapable of grasping anything, and so the man told them to stop where they were, and he would come to them. They huddled together, and waited; and he climbed down, and came in.

He was a young keeper, as luck would have it, and new to the business; and when he got in, he couldn't find them, and he wandered about, trying to get to them, and then he got lost. They caught sight of him, every now and then, rushing about the other side of the hedge, and he would see them, and rush to get to them, and they would wait there for about five minutes, and then he would reappear again in exactly the same spot, and ask them where they had been.

They had to wait till one of the old keepers came back from his dinner before they got out.

Harris said he thought it was a very fine maze, so far as he was a judge; and we agreed that we would try to get George to go into it, on our way back.

## AN UNSAVOURY INTERLUDE by Rudyard Kipling

IT WAS a maiden aunt of Stalky who sent him both
books, with the inscription, "To dearest Artie, on his
sixteenth birthday"; it was M'Turk who ordered their
hypothecation; and it was Beetle, returned from Bide-
ford, who flung them on the window-sill of Number
Five study with news that Bastable would advance but
ninepence on the two; *Eric; or, Little by Little*, being
almost as great a drug as *St. Winifred's*. "An' I don't
think much of your aunt. We're nearly out of car-
tridges, too—Artie, dear."

Whereupon Stalky rose up to grapple with him, but
M'Turk sat on Stalky's head, calling him a "pure-
minded boy" till peace was declared. As they were
grievously in arrears with a Latin prose, as it was a blaz-
ing July afternoon, and as they ought to have been at a
House cricket-match, they began to renew their acquaintance, intimate and unholy, with the volumes.

"Here we are!" said M'Turk. " 'Corporal punish-
ment produced on Eric the worst effects. He burned
*not* with remorse or regret'—make a note o' that, Beetle
—'but with shame and violent indignation. He glared'—
oh, naughty Eric! Let's get to where he goes in for
drink."

"Hold on half a shake. Here's another sample. 'The Sixth,' he says, 'is the palladium of all public schools.' But this lot"—Stalky rapped the gilded book—"can't prevent fellows drinkin' and stealin', an' lettin' fags out of window at night, an'—an' doin' what they please. Golly, what we've missed—not goin' to St. Wini-fred's! . . ."

"I'm sorry to see any boys of my House taking so little interest in their matches."

Mr. Prout could move very silently if he pleased, though that is no merit in a boy's eyes. He had flung open the study-door without knocking—another sin— and looked at them suspiciously. "Very sorry, indeed, I am to see you frowsting in your studies."

"We've been out ever since dinner, sir," said M'Turk wearily. One House-match is just like another, and their "ploy" of that week happened to be rabbit-shoot-ing with saloon-pistols.

"I can't see a ball when it's coming, sir," said Beetle. "I've had my gig-lamps smashed at the Nets till I got excused. I wasn't any good even as a fag, then, sir."

"Tuck is probably your form. Tuck and brewing. Why can't you three take any interest in the honour of your House?"

They had heard that phrase till they were wearied. The "honour of the House" was Prout's weak point, and they knew well how to flick him on the raw.

"If you order us to go down, sir, of course we'll go," said Stalky, with maddening politeness. But Prout knew better than that. He had tried the experiment once at a big match, when the three, self-isolated, stood to attention for half an hour in full view of all the visitors, to whom fags, subsidised for that end, pointed them out as victims of Prout's tyranny. And Prout was a sensitive man.

In the infinitely petty confederacies of the Common-room, King and Macrea, fellow House-masters, had borne it in upon him that by games, and games alone, was salvation wrought. Boys neglected were boys lost. They must be disciplined. Left to himself, Prout would have made a sympathetic House-master; but he was never so left, and, with the devilish insight of youth, the boys knew to whom they were indebted for his zeal.

"Must we go down, sir?" said M'Turk.

"I don't want to order you to do what a right-thinking boy should do gladly. I'm sorry." And he lurched out with some hazy impression that he had sown good seed on poor ground.

"Now what does he suppose is the use of that?" said Beetle.

"Oh, he's cracked. King jaws him in Common-room about not keepin' us up to the mark, and Macrea burbles about 'dithcipline,' an' old Heffy sits between 'em sweatin' big drops. I heard Oke [the Common-room butler] talking to Richards [Prout's House-servant] about it down in the basement the other day when I went down to bag some bread," said Stalky.

"What did Oke say?" demanded M'Turk, throwing *Eric* into a corner.

" 'Oh,' he said, 'they make more nise nor a nest full o' jackdaws, an' half of it like we'd no ears to our heads that waited on 'em. They talks over old Prout—

what he've done an' left undone about his boys. An'
how their boys be fine boys, an' his'n be dom bad.'
Well, Oke talked like that, you know, and Richards
got awf'ly wrathy. He has a down on King for something or other. 'Wonder why?"

"Why, King talks about Prout in form-room—makes
allusions, an' all that—only half the chaps are such asses
they can't see what he's drivin' at. And d'you remember what he said about the 'Casual House' last Tuesday? He meant us. They say he says perfectly beastly
things to his own House, making fun of Prout's," said
Beetle.

"Well, we didn't come here to mix up in their rows,"
M'Turk said wrathfully. "Who'll bathe after call-over?
King's takin' it in the cricket-field. Come on." Turkey
seized his straw and led the way.

They reached the sun-blistered pavilion over against
the gray Pebble Ridge just before roll-call, and, asking
no questions, gathered from King's voice and manner
that his House was on the road to victory.

"Ah, ha!" said he, turning to show the light of his
countenance. "Here we have the ornaments of the
Casual House at last. You consider cricket beneath you,
I believe"—the flannelled crowd sniggered—"and from
what I have seen this afternoon, I fancy many others
of your House hold the same view. And may I ask
what you purpose to do with your noble selves till
tea-time?"

"Going down to bathe, sir," said Stalky.

"And whence this sudden zeal for cleanliness? There
is nothing about you that particularly suggests it. In-

deed, so far as I remember—I may be at fault—but a
short time ago——"

"Five years, sir," said Beetle hotly.

King scowled. "One of you was that thing called a
water-funk. Yes, a water-funk. So now you wish to
wash? It is well. Cleanliness never injured a boy or—
a House. We will proceed to business," and he ad-
dressed himself to the call-over board.

"What the deuce did you say anything to him for,
Beetle?" said M'Turk angrily, as they strolled towards
the big, open sea-baths.

" 'Twasn't fair—remindin' one of bein' a water-funk.
My first term, too. Heaps of chaps are—when they
can't swim."

"Yes, you ass; but he saw he'd fetched you. You
ought never to answer King."

"But it wasn't fair, Stalky."

"My Hat! You've been here six years, and you expect fairness. Well, you *are* a dithering idiot."

A knot of King's boys, also bound for the baths,
hailed them, beseeching them to wash—for the honour
of their House.

"That's what comes of King's jawin' and messin'.
Those young animals wouldn't have thought of it unless
he'd put it into their heads. Now they'll be funny
about it for weeks," said Stalky. "Don't take any notice."

The boys came nearer, shouting an opprobrious word.
At last they moved to windward, ostentatiously holding
their noses.

"That's pretty," said Beetle. "They'll be sayin' our House stinks next."

When they returned from the baths, dampheaded, languid, at peace with the world, Beetle's forecast came only too true. They were met in the corridor by a fag —a common, Lower-Second fag—who at arm's length handed them a carefully wrapped piece of soap "with the compliments of King's House."

"Hold on," said Stalky, checking immediate attack. "Who put you up to this, Nixon? Rattray and White? [Those were two leaders in King's House.] Thank you. There's no answer."

"Oh, it's too sickening to have this kind o' rot shoved on to a chap. What's the sense of it? What's the fun of it?" said M'Turk.

"It will go on to the end of the term, though." Beetle wagged his head sorrowfully. He had worn many jests threadbare on his own account.

In a few days it became an established legend of the school that Prout's House did not wash and were therefore noisome. Mr. King was pleased to smile succulently in form when one of his boys drew aside from Beetle with certain gestures.

"There seems to be some disability attaching to you, my Beetle, or else why should Burton major withdraw, so to speak, the hem of his garments? I confess I am still in the dark. Will some one be good enough to enlighten me?"

Naturally, he was enlightened by half the Form.

"Extraordinary! Most extraordinary! However, each House has its traditions, with which I would not for the world interfere. *We* have a prejudice in favour of washing. Go on, Beetle—from '*Jugurtha tamen*'—and, if you can, avoid the more flagrant forms of guessing."

Prout's House was furious because Macrea's and Hartopp's Houses joined King's to insult them. They called a House-meeting after dinner—an excited and angry meeting of all save the prefects, whose dignity, though they sympathised, did not allow them to attend. They read ungrammatical resolutions, and made speeches beginning, "Gentlemen, we have met on this occasion," and ending with, "It's a beastly shame," precisely as Houses have done since time and schools began.

Number Five study attended, with its usual air of bland patronage. At last M'Turk, of the lanthorn jaws, delivered himself:

"You jabber and jaw and burble, and that's about all you can do. What's the good of it? King's House'll only gloat because they've drawn you, and King'll gloat, too. Besides, that resolution of Orrin's is chock-full of bad grammar, and King'll gloat over *that*."

"I thought you an' Beetle would put it right, an'—an' we'd post it in the corridor," said the composer meekly.

"*Pas si je le connai.* I'm not goin' to meddle with the biznai," said Beetle. "It's a gloat for King's House. Turkey's quite right."

"Well, won't Stalky, then?"

But Stalky puffed out his cheeks and squinted down his nose in the style of Panurge, and all he said was, "Oh, you abject burblers!"

"You're three beastly scabs!" was the instant retort of the democracy, and they went out amid execrations.

"This is piffling," said M'Turk. "Let's get out sallies, and go and shoot bunnies."

Three saloon-pistols, with a supply of bulleted breech-caps, were stored in Stalky's trunk, and this trunk was in their dormitory, and their dormitory was a three-bed attic one, opening out of a ten-bed establishment, which, in turn, communicated with the great range of dormitories that ran practically from one end of the College to the other. Macrea's House lay next to Prout's, King's next to Macrea's, and Hartopp's beyond that again. Carefully locked doors divided House from House, but each House, in its internal arrangements—the College had originally been a terrace of twelve large houses—was a replica of the next; one straight roof covering all.

They found Stalky's bed drawn out from the wall to the left of the dormer window, and the latter end of Richards protruding from a two-foot-square cupboard in the wall.

"What's all this? I've never noticed it before. What are you tryin' to do, Fatty?"

"Fillin' basins, Muster Corkran." Richards' voice was hollow and muffled. "They've been savin' me trouble. Yiss."

" 'Looks like it," said M'Turk. "Hi! You'll stick if you don't take care."

Richards backed puffing.

"I can't rache un. Yiss, 'tess a turncock, Muster M'Turk. They've took an' runned all the watter-pipes a storey higher in the houses—runned 'em all along under the 'ang of the heaves, like. Runned 'em in last holidays. *I* can't rache the turncock."

"Let me try," said Stalky, diving into the aperture.

"Slip 'ee to the left, then, Muster Corkran. Slip 'ee to the left, an' feel in the dark."

To the left Stalky wriggled, and saw a long line of lead-pipe disappearing up a triangular tunnel, whose roof was the rafters and boarding of the College roof, whose floor was sharp-edged joists, and whose side was the rough studding of the lath and plaster wall under the dormer.

" 'Rummy show. How far does it go?"

"Right along, Muster Corkran—right along from end to end. Her runs under the 'ang of the heaves. Have 'ee rached the stopcock yet? Mr. King got un put in to save us carryin' watter from downstairs to fill the basins. No place for a lusty man like old Richards. I'm tu thickabout to go ferritin'. Thank 'ee, Muster Cork-ran."

The water squirted through the tap just inside the cupboard, and, having filled the basins, the grateful Richards waddled away.

The boys sat round-eyed on their beds considering the possibilities of this trove. Two floors below them they could hear the hum of the angry House; for nothing is so still as a dormitory in mid-afternoon of a mid-summer term.

"It has been papered over till now." M'Turk examined the little door. "If we'd only known before!"

"I vote we go down and explore. No one will come up this time o' day. We needn't keep *cave*."

They crawled in, Stalky leading, drew the door behind them, and on all fours embarked on a dark and dirty road full of plaster, odd shavings, and all the raffle that builders leave in the waste-room of a house. The passage was perhaps three feet wide, and, except for the straggling light round the edges of the cupboards (there was one to each dormer), almost pitchy dark.

"Here's Macrea's House," said Stalky, his eye at the crack of the third cupboard. "I can see Barnes's name on his trunk. Don't make such a row, Beetle! We can get right to the end of the Coll. Come on! . . . We're in King's House now—I can see a bit of Rattray's trunk. How these beastly boards hurt one's knees!" They heard his nails scraping on plaster.

"That's the ceiling below. Look out! If we smashed that the plaster 'ud fall down in the lower dormitory," said Beetle.

"Let's," whispered M'Turk.

"An' be collared first thing? Not much. Why, I can shove my hand ever so far up between these boards."

Stalky thrust an arm to the elbow between the joists.

"No good stayin' here. I vote we go back and talk it over. It's a crummy place. 'Must say I'm grateful to King for his waterworks."

They crawled out, brushed one another clean, slid the saloon-pistols down a trouser-leg, and hurried forth to a deep and solitary Devonshire lane in whose flanks a boy might sometimes slay a young rabbit. They threw themselves down under the rank elder bushes, and began to think aloud.

"You know," said Stalky at last, sighting at a distant sparrow, "we could hide our sallies in there like anything."

"Huh!" Beetle snorted, choked, and gurgled. He had been silent since they left the dormitory.

"Did you ever read a book called *The History of a House* or something? I got it out of the library the other day. A Frenchwoman wrote it—Violet somebody. But it's translated, you know; and it's very interestin'. Tells you how a house is built."

"Well, if you're in a sweat to find that out, you can go down to the new cottages they're building for the coastguard."

"My Hat! I will." He felt in his pockets. "Give me tuppence, some one."

"Rot! Stay here, and don't mess about in the sun."

"Gi' me tuppence."

"I say, Beetle, you aren't stuffy about anything, are you?" said M'Turk, handing over the coppers. His tone was serious, for though Stalky often, and M'Turk occasionally, manoeuvred on his own account, Beetle had never been known to do so in all the history of the confederacy.

"No, I'm not. I'm thinking."

"Well, we'll come, too," said Stalky, with a general's suspicion of his aides.

" 'Don't want you."

"Oh, leave him alone. He's been taken worse with a poem," said M'Turk. "He'll go burbling down to the

Pebble Ridge and spit it all up in the study when he comes back."

"Then why did he want the tuppence, Turkey? He's gettin' too beastly independent. Hi! There's a bunny. No, it ain't. It's a cat, by Jove! You plug first."

Twenty minutes later a boy with a straw hat at the back of his head, and his hands in his pockets, was staring at workmen as they moved about a half-finished cottage. He produced some ferocious tobacco, and was passed from the forecourt into the interior, where he asked many questions.

"Well, let's have your beastly epic," said Turkey, as they burst into the study, to find Beetle deep in Viollet-le-Duc and some drawings. "We've had no end of a lark."

"Epic? What epic? I've been down to the coast-guard."

"No epic? Then we will slay you, O Beadle," said Stalky, moving to the attack. "You've got something up your sleeve. *I* know, when you talk in that tone!"

"Your Uncle Beetle"—with an attempt to imitate Stalky's war-voice—"is a Great Man."

"Oh, no; he jolly well isn't anything of the kind. You deceive yourself, Beetle. Scrag him, Turkey!"

"A Great Man," Beetle gurgled from the floor. "*You* are futile—look out for my tie!—futile burblers. I am the Great Man. I gloat. Ouch! Hear me!"

"Beetle, de-ah"—Stalky dropped unreservedly on Beetle's chest—"we love you, an' you're a poet. If I ever said you were a doggaroo, O apologise; but you know as well as we do that you can't do anything by yourself without mucking it."

"I've got a notion."

"And you'll spoil the whole show if you don't tell your Uncle Stalky. Cough it up, ducky, and we'll see what we can do. Notion, you fat impostor—I knew you had a notion when you went away! Turkey said it was a poem."

"I've found out how houses are built. Le' me get up. The floor-joists of one room are the ceiling-joists of the room below."

"Don't be so filthy technical."

"Well, the man told me. The floor is laid on top of those joists—those boards on edge that we crawled over —but the floor stops at a partition. Well, if you get behind a partition, same as you did in the attic, don't you see that you can shove anything you please under the floor between the floorboards and the lath and plaster of the ceiling below? Look here. I've drawn it."

He produced a rude sketch, sufficient to enlighten the allies. There is no part of the modern school curriculum that deals with architecture, and none of them had yet reflected whether floors and ceilings were hollow or solid. Outside his own immediate interests the boy is as ignorant as the savage he so admires; but he has also the savage's resource.

"I see," said Stalky. "I shoved my hand there. An' then?"

"An' then . . . They've been calling us stinkers, you know. We might shove somethin' under—sulphur, or something that stunk pretty bad—an' stink 'em out. I

know it can be done somehow." Beetle's eyes turned
to Stalky handling the diagrams.

"Stinks?" said Stalky interrogatively. Then his face
grew luminous with delight. "By gum! I've got it.
Horrid stinks! Turkey!" He leaped at the Irishman.
"This afternoon—just after Beetle went away! *She's*
the very thing!"

"Come to my arms, my beamish boy," carolled
M'Turk, and they fell into each other's arms dancing.
"Oh, frabjous day! Calloo, callay! She will! She will!"

"Hold on," said Beetle. "I don't understand."

"Dearr man! It shall, though. Oh, Artie, my pure-
souled youth, let us tell our darling Reggie about
Pestiferous Stinkadores."

"Not until after call-over. Come on!"

"I say," said Orrin stiffly, as they fell into their places
along the walls of the gymnasium. "The House are
goin' to hold another meeting."

"Hold away, then." Stalky's mind was elsewhere.

"It's about you three this time."

"All right, give 'em my love. . . . *Here, sir*," and he
tore down the corridor.

Gambolling like kids at play, with bounds and side-
starts, with caperings and curvettings, they led the
almost bursting Beetle to the rabbit-lane, and from
under a pile of stones drew forth the new-slain corpse
of a cat. Then did Beetle see the inner meaning of what
had gone before, and lifted up his voice in thanksgiving
for that the world held warriors so wise as Stalky and
M'Turk.

"Well-nourished old lady, ain't she?" said Stalky.

"How long d'you suppose it'll take her to get a bit whiff in a confined space?"

"Bit whiff! What a coarse brute you are!" said M'Turk. "Can't a poor pussy-cat get under King's dormitory floor to die without your pursuin' her with your foul innuendoes?"

"What did she die under the floor for?" said Beetle, looking to the future.

"Oh, they won't worry about *that* when they find her," said Stalky.

"A cat may look at a king." M'Turk rolled down the bank at his own jest. "Pussy, you don't know how useful you're goin' to be to three pure-souled, high-minded boys."

"They'll have to take up the floor for her, same as they did in Number Nine when the rat croaked. Big medicine—heap big medicine! Phew! Oh, Lord, I wish I could stop laughin'," said Beetle.

"Stinks! Hi, stinks! Clammy ones!" M'Turk gasped as he regained his place. "And"—the exquisite humour of it brought them sliding down together in a tangle—"it's all for the honour of the House, too!"

"An' they're holdin' another meetin'—on us," Stalky panted, his knees in the ditch and his face in the long grass. "Well, let's get the bullet out of her and hurry up. The sooner she's bedded out the better."

Between them they did some grisly work with a pen-knife; between them (ask not who buttoned her to his bosom) they took up the corpse and hastened back, Stalky arranging their plan of action at the full trot.

The afternoon sun, lying in broad patches on the

bed-rugs, saw three boys and an umbrella disappear into a dormitory wall. In five minutes they returned, brushed themselves all over, washed their hands, combed their hair, and descended.

"Are you sure you shoved her far enough under?" said M'Turk suddenly.

"Hang it, man, I shoved her the full length of my arm and Beetle's brolly. That must be about six feet. She's bung in the middle of King's big upper ten-bedder. Eligible central situation, *I* call it. She'll stink out his chaps, and Hartopp's and Macrea's, when she really begins to fume. I swear your Uncle Stalky is a great man. Do you realise what a great man he is, Beetle?"

"Well, I had the notion first, hadn't I, only——"

"You couldn't do it without your Uncle Stalky, could you?"

"They've been calling us stinkers for a week now," said M'Turk. "Oh, won't they catch it!"

"Stinker! Yah! Stink-ah!" rang down the corridor.

"And she's there," said Stalky, a hand on either boy's shoulder. "She—is—there, gettin' ready to surprise 'em. Presently she'll begin to whisper to 'em in their dreams. Then she'll whiff. Golly, how she'll whiff. Oblige me by thinkin' of it for two minutes."

They went to their study in more or less of silence. There they began to laugh—laugh as only boys can. They laughed with their foreheads on the tables, or on the floor; laughed at length, curled over the backs of chairs or clinging to a book-shelf; laughed themselves limp.

And in the middle of it Orrin entered on behalf of the House.

"Don't mind us, Orrin; sit down. You don't know how we respect and admire you. There's something about your pure, high, young forehead, full of the dreams of innocent boyhood, that's no end fetchin'. It is, indeed."

"The House sent me to give you this." He laid a folded sheet of paper on the table and retired with an awful front.

"It's the resolution! Oh, read it, some one. I'm too silly-sick with laughin' to see," said Beetle.

Stalky jerked it open with a precautionary sniff.

"Phew! Phew! Listen. *The House notices with pain and contempt the attitude of indiference*"—how many f's in indifference, Beetle?"

"Two for choice."

"Only one here—'*adopted by the occupants of Number Five Study in relation to the insults offered to Mr. Prout's House at the recent meeting in Number Twelve form-room, and the House hereby pass a vote of censure on the said study.*' That's all."

"And she bled all down my shirt, too!" said Beetle.

"An' I'm catty all over," said M'Turk, "though I washed twice."

"An' I nearly broke Beetle's brolly plantin' her where she would blossom!"

The situation was beyond speech, but not laughter. There was some attempt that night to demonstrate against the three in their dormitory; so they came forth.

"You see," Beetle began suavely as he loosened his

braces, "the trouble with you is that you're a set of un-thinkin' asses. You've no more brains than spidgers. We've told you that heaps of times, haven't we?"

"We'll give all three of you a dormitory lickin'. You always jaw at us as if you were prefects," cried one.

"Oh no, you won't," said Stalky, "because you know that if you did you'd get the worst of it sooner or later. *We* aren't in any hurry. *We* can afford to wait for our little revenges. You've made howlin' asses of yourselves, and just as soon as King gets hold of your precious resolution tomorrow you'll find that out. If you aren't sick an' sorry by to-morrow night, I'll—I'll eat my hat."

But or ever the dinner-bell rang the next day Prout's were sadly aware of their error. King received stray members of that House with an exaggerated attitude of fear. Did they purpose to cause him to be dismissed from the College by unanimous resolution? What were their views concerning the government of the school, that he might hasten to give effect to them? He would not offend them for worlds; but he feared—he sadly feared—that his own House, who did not pass resolu-tions (but washed), might somewhat deride.

King was a happy man, and his House, basking in the favour of his smile, made that afternoon a long penance to the misled Prout's. And Prout himself, with a dull and lowering visage, tried to think out the rights and wrongs of it all, only plunging deeper into bewil-derment. Why should his House be called "stinkers"? Truly, it was a small thing, but he had been trained to believe that straws show which way the wind blows, and that there is no smoke without fire. He approached

King in Common-room with a sense of injustice, but King was pleased to be full of airy persiflage that tide, and brilliantly danced dialectical rings round Prout.

"Now," said Stalky at bedtime, making pilgrimage through the dormitories before the prefects came up, "*now* what have you got to say for yourselves? Foster, Carton, Finch, Longbridge, Marlin, Brett! I heard you chaps catchin' it from King—he made hay of you—an' all you could do was to wriggle an' grin an' say, 'Yes, sir,' an' 'No, sir,' an' 'Oh, sir,' an' 'Please, sir'! You an' your resolution! Urh!"

"Oh, shut up, Stalky."

"Not a bit of it. You're a gaudy lot of resolutionists, you are! You've made a sweet mess of it. Perhaps you'll have the decency to leave us alone next time."

Here the House grew angry, and in many voices pointed out how this blunder would never have come to pass if Number Five study had helped them from the first.

"But you chaps are so beastly conceited, an'—an' you swaggered into the meetin' as if we were a lot of idiots," growled Orrin of the resolution.

"That's precisely what you *are!* That's what we've been tryin' to hammer into your thick heads all this time," said Stalky. "Never mind, we'll forgive you. Cheer up. You can't help bein' asses, you know," and, the enemy's flank deftly turned, Stalky hopped into bed.

That night was the first of sorrow among the jubilant King's. By some accident of under-floor draughts the cat did not vex the dormitory beneath which she lay, but the next one to the right; stealing on the air rather as a pale-blue sensation than as any poignant offence. But the mere adumbration of an odour is enough for the sensitive nose and clean tongue of youth. Decency demands that we draw several carbolised sheets over what the dormitory said to Mr. King and what Mr. King replied. He was genuinely proud of his House and fastidious in all that concerned their well-being. He came; he sniffed; he said things. Next morning a boy in that dormitory confided to his bosom friend, a fag of Macrea's, that there was trouble in their midst which King would fain keep secret.

But Macrea's boy had also a bosom friend in Prout's, a shock-headed fag of malignant disposition, who, when he had wormed out the secret, told—told it in a high-pitched treble that rang along the corridor like a bat's squeak.

"An'—an' they've been calling us 'stinkers' all this week. Why, Harland minor says they simply can't sleep in his dormitory for the stink. Come on!"

"With one shout and with one cry" Prout's juniors hurled themselves into the war, and through the interval between first and second lesson some fifty twelve-year-olds were embroiled on the gravel outside King's windows to a tune whose *leit-motif* was the word "stinker."

"Hark to the minute-gun at sea!" said Stalky. They were in their study collecting books for second lesson— Latin, with King. "I thought his azure brow was a bit cloudy at prayers.

> She is comin', sister Mary,
> She is——"

"If they make such a row now, what will they do when she really begins to look up an' take notice?"

"Well, no vulgar repartee, Beetle. All we want is to keep out of this row like gentlemen."

"' 'Tis but a little faded flower.' Where's my Horace? Look here, I don't understand what she means by stinkin' out Rattray's dormitory first. We holed in under White's, didn't we?" asked M'Turk, with a wrinkled brow.

"Skittish little thing. She's rompin' about all over the place, I suppose."

"My Aunt! King'll be a cheerful customer at second lesson. I haven't prepared my Horace one little bit, either," said Beetle. "Come on!"

They were outside the form-room door now. It was within five minutes of the bell, and King might arrive at any moment.

Turkey elbowed into a cohort of scuffling fags, cut out Thornton tertius (he that had been Harland's bosom friend), and bade him tell his tale.

It was a simple one, interrupted by tears. Many of King's House had already battered him for libel.

"Oh, it's nothing," M'Turk cried. "He says that King's House stinks. That's all."

"Stale!" Stalky shouted. "We knew that years ago, only we didn't choose to run about shoutin' 'Stinker!' We've got some manners, if they haven't. Catch a fag, Turkey, and make sure of it."

Turkey's long arm closed on a hurried and anxious ornament of the Lower Second.

"Oh, M'Turk, please let me go. I don't stink—I swear I don't!"

"Guilty conscience!" cried Beetle. "Who said you did?"

"What d'you make of it?" Stalky punted the small boy into Beetle's arms.

"Snf! Snf! He does, though. I think it's leprosy—or thrush. P'raps it's both. Take it away."

"Indeed, Master Beetle"—King generally came to the House-door for a minute or two as the bell rang—"we are vastly indebted to you for your diagnosis, which seems to reflect almost as much credit on the natural unwholesomeness of your mind as it does upon your pitiful ignorance of the diseases of which you discourse so glibly. We will, however, test your knowledge in other directions."

That was a merry lesson, but, in his haste to scarify Beetle, King clean neglected to give him an imposition, and since at the same time he supplied him with many priceless adjectives for later use, Beetle was well content, and applied himself most seriously throughout third lesson (algebra with little Hartopp) to composing a poem entitled "The Lazar-house."

After dinner King took his House to bathe in the sea off the Pebble Ridge. It was an old promise; but he wished he could have evaded it, for all Prout's lined up by the Fives Court and cheered with intention. In his absence not less than half the school invaded the infected dormitory to draw their own conclusions. The cat had gained in the last twelve hours, but a battlefield of the fifth day could not have been so flamboyant as the spies reported.

"My word, she *is* doin' herself proud," said Stalky. "Did you ever smell anything like it? Ah, an' she isn't under White's dormitory at all yet."

"But she will be. Give her time," said Beetle. "She'll twine like a giddy honeysuckle. What howlin' Lazarites they are! No House is justified in makin' itself a stench in the nostrils of decent——"

"High-minded, pure-souled boys. *Do* you burn with remorse and regret?" said M'Turk, as they hastened to meet the House coming up from the sea. King had deserted it, so speech was unfettered. Round its front played a crowd of skirmishers—all Houses mixed—flying, re-forming, shrieking insults. On its tortured flanks marched the Hoplites, seniors hurling jests one after another—simple and primitive jests of the Stone Age. To these the three added themselves, dispassionately, with an air of aloofness, almost sadly.

"And they look all right, too," said Stalky. "It can't be Rattray, can it? Rattray?"

No answer.

"Rattray, dear? He seems stuffy about something or other. Look here, old man, we don't bear any malice about your sending that soap to us last week, do we? Be cheerful, Rat. You can live this down all right. I dare say it's only a few fags. Your House *is* so beastly slack, though."

"You aren't going back to the House, are you?" said M'Turk. The victims desired nothing better. "You've simply no conception of the reek up there. Of course, frowzin' as you do, you wouldn't notice it; but, after this nice wash and the clean, fresh air, even you'd be upset. 'Much better camp on the Burrows. We'll get you some straw. Shall we?" The House hurried in to the tune of "John Brown's body," sung by loving school-mates, and barricaded themselves in their form-room. Straightway Stalky chalked a large cross, with "Lord, have mercy upon us," on the door, and left King to find it.

The wind shifted that night and wafted a carrion-reek into Macrea's dormitories; so that boys in night-gowns pounded on the locked door between the Houses, entreating King's to wash. Number Five study went to second lesson with not more than half a pound of camphor apiece in their clothing; and King, too wary to ask for explanations, gibbered awhile and hurled them forth. So Beetle finished yet another poem at peace in the study.

"They're usin' carbolic now. Malpas told me," said Stalky. "King thinks it's the drains."

"She'll need a lot o' carbolic," said M'Turk. "No harm tryin', I suppose. It keeps King out of mischief."

"I swear I thought he was goin' to kill me when I sniffed just now. He didn't mind Burton major sniffin' at me the other day, though. He never stopped Alexander howlin' 'Stinker!' into our form-room before—before we doctored 'em. He just grinned," said Stalky. "What was he frothing over you for, Beetle?"

"Aha! That was my subtle jape. I had him on toast. You know he always jaws about the learned Lipsius."

" 'Who at the age of four'—*that* chap?" said M'Turk.

"Yes. Whenever he hears I've written a poem. Well, just as I was sittin' down, I whispered. 'How is our learned Lipsius?' to Burton major. Old Butt grinned like an owl. He didn't know what I was drivin' at; but King jolly well did. That was really why he hove us out. Ain't you grateful? Now shut up. I'm goin' to write the 'Ballad of the Learned Lipsius.'"

"Keep clear of anything coarse, then," said Stalky. "I shouldn't like to be coarse on this happy occasion."

"Not for wo-orlds. What rhymes to 'stenches,' some one?"

In Common-room at lunch King discoursed acridly to Prout of boys with prurient minds, who perverted their few and baleful talents to sap discipline and corrupt their equals, to deal in foul imagery and destroy reverence.

"But you didn't seem to consider this when your House called us—ah—stinkers. If you hadn't assured me that you never interfere with another man's House, I should almost believe that it was a few casual remarks of yours that started all this nonsense."

Prout had endured much, for King always took his temper to meals.

"You spoke to Beetle yourself, didn't you? Something about not bathing, and being a water-funk?" the school chaplain put in. "I was scoring in the pavilion that day."

"I may have—jestingly. I really don't pretend to remember every remark I let fall among small boys; and full well I know the Beetle has no feelings to be hurt."

"Maybe; but he, or they—it comes to the same thing

—have the fiend's own knack of discovering a man's weak place. I confess I rather go out of my way to conciliate Number Five study. It may be soft, but so far, I believe, I am the only man here whom they haven't maddened by their—well—attentions."

"That is all beside the point. I flatter myself I can deal with them alone as occasion arises. But if they feel themselves morally supported by those who should wield an absolute and openhanded justice, then I say that my lot is indeed a hard one. Of all things I detest, I admit that anything verging on disloyalty among ourselves is the first."

The Common-room looked at one another out of the corners of their eyes, and Prout blushed.

"I deny it absolutely," he said. "Er—in fact, I own that I personally object to all three of them. It is not fair, therefore, to——"

"How long do you propose to allow it?" said King.

"But surely," said Macrea, deserting his usual ally, "the blame, if there be any, rests with you, King. You can't hold them responsible for the—you prefer the good old Anglo-Saxon, I believe—stink in your House. My boys are complaining of it now."

"What can you expect? You know what boys are. Naturally they take advantage of what to them is a heaven-sent opportunity," said little Hartopp. "What *is* the trouble in your dormitories, King?"

Mr. King explained that as he had made it the one rule of his life never to interfere with another man's House, so he expected not to be too patently interfered with. They might be interested to learn—here the chaplain heaved a weary sigh—that he had taken all steps that, in his poor judgment, would meet the needs of the case. Nay, further, he had himself expended, with no thought of reimbursement, sums, the amount of which he would not specify, on disinfectants. This he had done because he knew by bitter—by most bitter—experience that the management of the College was slack, dilatory, and inefficient. He might even add almost as slack as the administration of certain Houses which now thought fit to sit in judgment on his actions. With a short summary of his scholastic career, and a *précis* of his qualifications, including his degrees, he withdrew, slamming the door.

"Heigho!" said the chaplain. "Ours is a dwarfing life —a belittling life, my brethren. God help all schoolmasters! They need it."

"I don't like the boys, I own"—Prout dug viciously with his fork into the table-cloth—"and I don't pretend to be a strong man, as you know. But I confess I can't see any reason why I should take steps against Stalky and the others because King happens to be annoyed by—by——"

"Falling into the pit he has digged," said little Hartopp. "Certainly not, Prout. No one accuses you of setting one House against another through sheer idleness."

"A belittling life—a belittling life." The chaplain rose. "I go to correct French exercises. By dinner King will have scored off some unlucky child of thirteen; he will repeat to us every word of his brilliant repartees, and all will be well."

"But about those three. Are they so prurient-minded?"

"Nonsense," said little Hartopp. "If you thought for a minute, Prout, you would see that the 'precocious flow of fetid imagery' that King complains of is borrowed wholesale from King. *He* 'nursed the pinion that impelled the steel.' Naturally he does not approve. Come into the smoking-room for a minute. It isn't fair to listen to boys; but they should be now rubbing it into King's House outside. Little things please little minds."

The dingy den off the Common-room was never used for anything except gowns. Its windows were ground glass; one could not see out of it, but one could hear almost every word on the gravel outside. A light and wary footstep came up from Number Five.

"Rattray!" in a subdued voice—Rattray's study fronted that way. "D'you know if Mr. King's anywhere about? I've got a——" M'Turk discreetly left the end of his sentence open.

"No. He's gone out," said Rattray unguardedly.

"Ah! The learned Lipsius is airing himself, is he? His Royal Highness has gone to fumigate." M'Turk climbed on the railings, where he held forth like the never-wearied rook.

"Now in all the Coll. there was no stink like the stink of King's House, for it stank vehemently and none knew what to make of it. Save King. And he washed the fags *privatim et seriatim*. In the fishpools of Heshbon washed he them, with an apron about his loins."

"Shut up, you mad Irishman!" There was the sound of a golf-ball spurting up the gravel.

"It's no good getting wrathy, Rattray. We've come to jape with you. Come on, Beetle. They're all at home. You can wind 'em."

"Where's the Pomposo Stinkadore? 'Tisn't safe for a pure-souled, high-minded boy to be seen round his House these days. Gone out, has he? Never mind. I'll do the best I can, Rattray. I'm *in loco parentis* just now."

("One for you, Prout," whispered Macrea, for this was Mr. Prout's pet phrase.)

"I have a few words to impart to you, my young friend. We will discourse together awhile."

Here the listening Prout sputtered: Beetle, in a strained voice, had chosen a favourite gambit of King's.

"I repeat, Master Rattray, we will confer, and the matter of our discourse shall not be stinks, for that is a loathsome and obscene word. We will, with your good leave—granted, I trust, Master Rattray, granted, I trust—study this—this scabrous upheaval of latent demoralisation. What impresses me most is not so much the blatant indecency with which you swagger abroad under your load of putrescence" (you must imagine this discourse punctuated with golf-balls, but old Rattray was ever a bad shot) "as the cynical immorality with which you revel in your abhorrent aromas. Far be it from me to interfere with another's House——"

("Good Lord!" said Prout, "but this *is* King.")

"Line for line, letter for letter. Listen," said little Hartopp.)

"But to say that you stink, as certain lewd fellows of the baser sort aver, is to say nothing—less than nothing. In the absence of your beloved House-master, for whom no one has a higher regard than myself, I will, if you will allow me, explain the grossness—the unparalleled enormity—the appalling fetor of the stenches (I believe in the good old Anglo-Saxon word), stenches, sir, with which you have seen fit to infect your House. . . . Oh, bother! I've forgotten the rest, but it was very beautiful. Aren't you grateful to us for labourin' with you this way, Rattray? Lots of chaps 'ud never have taken the trouble, but we're grateful, Rattray."

"Yes, we're horrid grateful," grunted M'Turk. "We don't forget that soap. We're polite. Why ain't you polite, Rat?"

"Hallo!" Stalky cantered up, his cap over one eye. "Exhortin' the Whiffers, eh? I'm afraid they're too far gone to repent. Rattray! White! Perowne! Malpas! No answer. This is distressin'. This is truly distressin'. Bring out your dead, you glandered lepers!"

"You think yourself funny, don't you?" said Rattray, stung from his dignity by this last. "It's only a rat or something under the floor. We're going to have it up to-morrow."

"Don't try to shuffle it off on a poor dumb animal, and dead, too. I loathe prevarication. 'Pon my soul, Rattray——"

"Hold on. The Hartoffles never said ' 'Pon my soul' in all his little life," said Beetle critically.

("Ah!" said Prout to little Hartopp.)

"Upon my word, sir, upon my word, sir, I expected

better things of you, Rattray. Why can you not own up to your misdeeds like a man? Have *I* ever shown any lack of confidence in *you?*"

("It's not brutality," murmured little Hartopp, as though answering a question no one had asked. "It's boy; only boy.")

"And this was the House." Stalky changed from a pecking, fluttering voice to tragic earnestness. "This was the—the—open cesspit that dared to call us 'stinkers.' And now—and now, it tries to shelter itself behind a dead rat. You annoy me, Rattray. You disgust me! You irritate me unspeakably! Thank Heaven, I am a man of equable temper——"

("This is to your address, Macrea," said Prout.

"I fear so, I fear so.")

"Or I should scarcely be able to contain myself before your mocking visage."

"*Cave!*" in an undertone. Beetle had spied King sailing down the corridor.

"And what may you be doing here, my little friends?" the House-master began. "I had a fleeting notion—correct me if I am wrong (the listeners with one accord choked)—that if I found you outside my House I should visit you with dire pains and penalties."

"We were just goin' for a walk, sir," said Beetle.

"And you stopped to speak to Rattray *en route?*"

"Yes, sir. We've been throwing golf-balls," said Rattray, coming out of the study.

("Old Rat is more of a diplomat than I thought. So far he is strictly within the truth," said little Hartopp. "Observe the ethics of it, Prout.")

"Oh, you were sporting with them, were you? I must say I do not envy you your choice of associates. I fancy they might have been engaged in some of the prurient discourse with which they have been so disgustingly free of late. I should strongly advise you to direct your steps most carefully in the future. Pick up those golf-balls." He passed on.

Next day Richards, who had been a carpenter in the Navy, and to whom odd jobs were confided, was ordered to take up a dormitory floor; for Mr. King held that something must have died there.

"We need not neglect all our work for a trumpery incident of this nature; though I am quite aware that little things please little minds. Yes, I have decreed the boards to be taken up after lunch under Richards' auspices. I have no doubt it will be vastly interesting to a certain type of so-called intellect; but any boy of my House or another's found on the dormitory stairs will *ipso facto* render himself liable to three hundred lines."

The boys did not collect on the stairs, but most of them waited outside King's. Richards had been bound to cry the news from the attic window, and, if possible, to exhibit the corpse.

" 'Tis a cat, a dead cat!" Richards' face showed purple at the window. He had been in the chamber of death and on his knees for some time.

"Cat be blowed!" cried M'Turk. "It's a dead fag left over from last term. Three cheers for King's dead fag!"

They cheered lustily.

"Show it, show it! Let's have a squint at it!" yelled the juniors. "Give her to the Bug-hunters. [This was the Natural History Society.] The cat looked at the King—and died of it! Hoosh! Yai! Yaow! Maiow! Ftzz!" were some of the cries that followed.

Again Richards appeared.

"She've been"—he checked himself suddenly—"dead a long taime."

The school roared.

"Well, come on out for a walk," said Stalky in a well-chosen pause. "It's all very disgustin', and I do hope that the Lazar-house won't do it again."

"Do what?" a King's boy cried furiously.

"Kill a poor innocent cat every time you want to get off washing. It's awfully hard to distinguish between you as it is. I prefer the cat, I must say. She isn't quite so whiff. What are you goin' to do, Beetle?"

"*Je vais gloater. Je vais gloater tout le* blessed afternoon. *Jamais j'ai gloaté comme je gloater ai aujourd' hui. Nous bunkerons aux* bunkers."

And it seemed good to them so to do.

Down in the basement, where the gas flickers and the boots stand in racks, Richards, amid his blacking-brushes, held forth to Oke of the Common-room, Gumbly of the dining-halls, and fair Lena of the laundry.

"Yiss. Her were in a shockin' staate an' condition. Her nigh made me sick, I tal 'ee. But I rowted un out, and I rowted un out, an' I made all shipshape, though her smelt like to bilges."

"Her died mousin', I rackon, poor thing," said Lena.

"Then her moused different to any made cat o' God's world, Lena. I up with the top-board, an' she were lying on her back, an' I turned un ovver with the brume-handle, an' 'twas her back was all covered with the plaster from 'twixt the lathin'. Yiss, I tal 'ee. An' under her head there lay, like, so's to say, a little pillow o' plaster druv up in front of her by raison of her slidin' along on her back. No cat niver went mousin' on her back, Lena. Some one had shoved her along right underneath, so far as they could shove un. Cats don't make themselves pillows for to die on. Shoved along, she were, when she was settin' for to be cold, laike."

"Oh, yeou'm too clever to live, Fatty. Yeou go get wed an' taught some sense," said Lena, the affianced of Gumbly.

" 'Larned a little 'fore iver some maidens was born. Sarved in the Queen's Navy, I have, where yeou'm taught to use your eyes. Yeou go 'tend your own business, Lena."

"Do 'ee mean what you'm been tellin' us?" said Oke.

"Ask me no questions, I'll give 'ee no lies. Bullet-hole clane thru from side to side, an' tu heart-ribs broke like withies. I seed un when I turned un ovver. They'm clever, oh, they'm clever, but they'm not too clever for old Richards! 'Twas on the born tip o' my tongue to tell, tu, but . . . he said us niver washed, he did. Let his dom boys call us 'stinkers,' he did. Sarved un dom well raight, I say!"

Richards spat on a fresh boot and fell to his work, chuckling.

## HORSESHOES by Ring Lardner

THE series ended Tuesday, but I had stayed in Philadelphia an extra day on the chance of there being some follow-up stuff worth sending. Nothing had broken loose; so I filed some stuff about what the Athletics and Giants were going to do with their dough, and then caught the eight o'clock train for Chicago.

Having passed up supper in order to get my story away and grab the train, I went to the buffet car right after I'd planted my grips. I sat down at one of the tables and ordered a sandwich. Four salesmen were playing rum at the other table and all the chairs in the car were occupied; so it didn't surprise me when somebody flopped down in the seat opposite me.

I looked up from my paper and with a little thrill recognized my companion. Now I've been experting round the country with ball players so much that it doesn't usually excite me to meet one face to face, even if he's a star. I can talk with Tyrus without getting all fussed up. But this particular player had jumped from obscurity to fame so suddenly and had played such an important though brief part in the recent argument between the Macks and McGraws that I couldn't help being a little awed by his proximity.

It was none other than Grimes, the utility outfielder Connie had been forced to use in the last game because of the injury to Joyce—Grimes, whose miraculous catch in the eleventh inning had robbed Parker of a home run and the Giants of victory, and whose own homer—a fluky one—had given the Athletics another World's Championship.

I had met Grimes one day during the spring he was with the Cubs, but I knew he wouldn't remember me. A ball player never recalls a reporter's face on less than six introductions or his name on less than twenty. However, I resolved to speak to him, and had just mustered sufficient courage to open a conversation when he saved me the trouble.

"Whose picture have they got there?" he asked, pointing to my paper.

"Speed Parker's," I replied.

"What do they say about him?" asked Grimes.

"I'll read it to you," I said:

" 'Speed Parker, McGraw's great third baseman, is ill in a local hospital with nervous prostration, the result of the strain of the World's Series, in which he played such a stellar rôle. Parker is in such a dangerous condition that no one is allowed to see him. Members of the New York team and fans from Gotham called at the hospital to-day, but were unable to gain admittance to his ward. Philadelphians hope he will recover speedily and will suffer no permanent ill effects from his sickness, for he won their admiration by his work in the series, though he was on a rival team. A lucky catch by Grimes, the Athletics' substitute outfielder, was all that prevented Parker from winning the title for New York. According to Manager Mack, of the champions, the series would have been over in four games but for Parker's wonderful exhibition of nerve and—' "

"That'll be plenty," Grimes interrupted. "And that's just what you might expect from one o' them dough-headed reporters. If all the baseball writers was where they belonged they'd have to build an annex to Matteawan."

I kept my temper with very little effort—it takes more than a peevish ball player's remarks to insult one of our fraternity; but I didn't exactly understand his peeve.

"Doesn't Parker deserve the bouquet?" I asked.

"Oh, they can boost him all they want to," said Grimes; "but when they call that catch lucky and don't mention the fact that Parker is the luckiest guy in the world, somethin' must be wrong with 'em. Did you see the serious?"

"No," I lied glibly, hoping to draw from him the cause of his grouch.

"Well," he said, "you sure missed somethin'. They never was a serious like it before and they won't never be one again. It went the full seven games and every game was a bear. They was one big innin' every day and Parker was the big cheese in it. Just as Connie says, the Ath-a-letics would of cleaned 'em in four games but for Parker; but it wasn't because he's a great ball player—it was because he was born with a knife, fork and spoon in his mouth, and a rabbit's foot hung round his neck.

"You may not know it, but I'm Grimes, the guy that

made the lucky catch. I'm the guy that won the serious with a hit—a home-run hit; and I'm here to tell you that if I'd had one-tenth o' Parker's luck they'd of heard about me long before yesterday. They say my homer was lucky. Maybe it was; but, believe me, it was time things broke for me. They been breakin' for him all his life."

"Well," I said, "his luck must have gone back on him if he's in a hospital with nervous prostration."

"Nervous prostration nothin'," said Grimes. "He's in a hospital because his face is all out o' shape and he's ashamed to appear on the street. I don't usually do so much talkin' and I'm ravin' a little to-night because I've had a couple o' drinks; but——"

"Have another," said I, ringing for the waiter, "and talk some more."

"I made two hits yesterday," Grimes went on, "but the crowd only seen one. I busted up the game and the serious with the one they seen. The one they didn't see was the one I busted up a guy's map with—and Speed Parker was the guy. That's why he's in a hospital. He may be able to play ball next year; but I'll bet my share o' the dough that McGraw won't reco'nize him when he shows up at Marlin in the spring."

"When did this come off?" I asked. "And why?"

"It come off outside the clubhouse after yesterday's battle," he said; "and I hit him because he called me a name—a name I won't stand for from him."

"What did he call you?" I queried, expecting to hear

one of the delicate epithets usually applied by conquered to conqueror on the diamond.

" 'Horseshoes!' " was Grimes' amazing reply.

"But, good Lord!" I remonstrated, "I've heard of ball players calling each other that, and Lucky Stiff, and Fourleaf Clover, ever since I was a foot high, and I never knew them to start fights about it."

"Well," said Grimes, "I might as well give you all the dope; and then if you don't think I was justified I'll pay your fare from here to wherever you're goin'. I don't want you to think I'm kickin' about trifles—or that I'm kickin' at all, for that matter. I just want to prove to you that he didn't have no license to pull that Horseshoes stuff on me and that I only give him what was comin' to him."

"Go ahead and shoot," said I.

"Give us some more o' the same," said Grimes to the passing waiter. And then he told me about it.

Maybe you've heard that me and Speed Parker was raised in the same town—Ishpeming, Michigan. We was kids together, and though he done all the devilment I got all the lickin's. When we was about twelve years old Speed throwed a rotten egg at the teacher and I got expelled. That made me sick o' schools and I wouldn't never go to one again, though my ol' man beat me up and the truant officers threatened to have me hung.

Well, while Speed was learnin' what was the principal products o' New Hampshire and Texas I was workin' round the freighthouse and drivin' a dray.

We'd both been playin' ball all our lives; and when the town organized a semi-pro club we got jobs with it. We was to draw two bucks apiece for each game and they played every Sunday. We played four games before we got our first pay. They was a hole in my pants pocket as big as the home plate, but I forgot about it and put the dough in there. It wasn't there when I got home. Speed didn't have no hole in his pocket— you can bet on that! Afterward the club hired a good outfielder and I was canned. They was huntin' for another third baseman too; but, o' course, they didn't find none and Speed held his job.

The next year they started the Northern Peninsula League. We landed with the home team. The league opened in May and blowed up the third week in June. They paid off all the outsiders first and then had just money enough left to settle with one of us two Ishpeming guys. The night they done the payin' I was out to my uncle's farm, so they settled with Speed and told me I'd have to wait for mine. I'm still waitin'!

Gene Higgins, who was manager o' the Battle Creek Club, lived in Houghton, and that winter we goes over and strikes him for a job. He give it to us and we busted in together two years ago last spring.

I had a good year down there. I hit over .300 and stole all the bases in sight. Speed got along good too, and they was several big-league scouts lookin' us over. The Chicago Cubs bought Speed outright and four clubs put in a draft for me. Three of 'em—Cleveland and the New York Giants and the Boston Nationals— needed outfielders bad, and it would of been a pipe for me to of made good with any of 'em. But who do you think got me? The same Chicago Cubs; and the only outfielders they had at that time was Schulte and Leach and Good and Williams and Stewart, and one or two others.

Well, I didn't figure I was any worse off than Speed. The Cubs had Zimmerman at third base and it didn't look like they was any danger of a busher beatin' him out; but Zimmerman goes and breaks his leg the second day o' the season—that's a year ago last April—and Speed jumps right in as a regular. Do you think anything like that could happen to Schulte or Leach, or any o' them outfielders? No, sir! I wore out my uniform slidin' up and down the bench and wonderin' whether they'd ship me to Fort Worth or Siberia.

Now I want to tell you about the miserable luck Speed had right off the reel. We was playin' at St. Louis. They had a one-run lead in the eight, when their pitcher walked Speed with one out. Saier hits a high fly to centre and Parker starts with the crack o' the bat. Both coachers was yellin' at him to go back, but he thought they was two out and he was clear round to third base when the ball come down. And Oakes muffs it! O' course he scored and the game was tied up.

Parker come in to the bench like he'd did something wonderful.

"Did you think they was two out?" ast Hank.

"No," says Speed, blushin'.

"Then what did you run for?" says Hank.

"I had a hunch he was goin' to drop the ball," says Speed; and Hank pretty near falls off the bench.

The next day he come up with one out and the sacks full, and the score tied in the sixth. He smashes one on the ground straight at Hauser and it looked like a cinch double play; but just as Hauser was goin' to grab it the ball hit a rough spot and hopped a mile over his head. It got between Oakes and Magee and went clear to the fence. Three guys scored and Speed pulled up at third. The papers come out and said the game was won by a three-bagger from the bat o' Parker, the Cubs' sensational kid third baseman. Gosh!

We go home to Chi and are havin' a hot battle with Pittsburgh. This time Speed's turn come when they was two on and two out, and Pittsburgh a run to the good—I think it was the eighth innin'. Cooper gives him a fast one and he hits it straight up in the air. O' course the runners started goin', but it looked hopeless because they wasn't no wind or high sky to bother anybody. Mowrey and Gibson both goes after the ball; and just as Mowrey was set for the catch Gibson bumps into him and they both fall down. Two runs scored and Speed got to second. Then what does he do but try to steal third—with two out too! And Gibson's peg pretty near hits the left field seats on the fly.

When Speed comes to the bench Hank says:

"If I was you I'd quit playin' ball and go to Monte Carlo."

"What for?" says Speed.

"You're so dam' lucky!" says Hank.

"So is Ty Cobb," says Speed. That's how he hated himself!

First trip to Cincy we run into a couple of old Ishpeming boys. They took us out one night, and about twelve o'clock I said we'd have to go back to the hotel or we'd get fined. Speed said I had cold feet and he stuck with the boys. I went back alone and Hank caught me comin' in and put a fifty-dollar plaster on me. Speed stayed out all night long and Hank never knowed it. I says to myself: "Wait till he gets out there and tries to play ball without no sleep!" But the game that day was called off on account o' rain. Can you beat it?

I remember what he got away with the next afternoon the same as though it happened yesterday. In the second innin' they walked him with nobody down, and he took a big lead off first base like he always does. Benton throwed over there three or four times to scare him back, and the last time he throwed, Hobby hid the ball. The coacher seen it and told Speed to hold the bag; but he didn't pay no attention. He started leadin' right off again and Hobby tried to tag him, but the ball slipped out of his hand and rolled about a yard away. Parker had plenty o' time to get back; but, instead o' that, he starts for second. Hobby picked up the ball and shot it down to Groh—and Groh made a square muff.

Parker slides into the bag safe and then gets up and throws out his chest like he'd made the greatest play ever. When the ball's throwed back to Benton, Speed leads off about thirty foot and stands there in a trance. Clarke signs for a pitch-out and pegs down to second to nip him. He was caught flatfooted—that is, he would of been with a decent throw; but Clarke's peg went pretty near to Latonia. Speed scored and strutted over to receive our hearty congratulations. Some o' the boys was laughin' and he thought they was laughin' with him instead of at him.

It was in the ninth, though, that he got by with one o' the worst I ever seen. The Reds was a run behind and Marsans was on third base with two out. Hobby, I think it was, hit one on the ground right at Speed and he picked it up clean. The crowd all got up and started for the exits. Marsans run toward the plate in the faint hope that the peg to first would be wild. All of a sudden the boys on the Cincy bench begun yellin' at him to slide, and he done so. He was way past the plate when Speed's throw got to Archer. The bonehead had shot the ball home instead o' to first base, thinkin' they was only one down. We was all crazy, believin' his nut play had let 'em tie it up; but he comes terin' in, tellin' Archer to tag Marsans. So Jim walks over and tags the Cuban, who was brushin' off his uniform.

"You're out!" says Klem. "You never touched the plate."

I guess Marsans knowed the umps was right because he didn't make much of a holler. But Speed sure got a pannin' in the clubhouse.

"I suppose you knowed he was goin' to miss the plate!" says Hank sarcastic as he could.

Everybody on the club roasted him, but it didn't do no good.

Well, you know what happened to me. I only got

into one game with the Cubs—one afternoon when
Leach was sick. We was playin' the Boston bunch and
Tyler was workin' against us. I always had trouble with
lefthanders and this was one of his good days. I couldn't
see what he throwed up there. I got one foul durin'
the afternoon's entertainment; and the wind was blowin'
a hundred-mile gale, so that the best outfielder in the
world couldn't judge a fly ball. That Boston bunch
must of hit fifty of 'em and they all come to my field.

If I caught any I've forgot about it. Couple o' days
after that I got notice o' my release to Indianapolis.

Parker kept right on all season doin' the blamedest
things you ever heard of and gettin' by with 'em. One
o' the boys told me about it later. If they was playin'
a double-header in St. Louis, with the thermometer at
130 degrees, he'd get put out by the umps in the first
innin' o' the first game. If he started to steal the
catcher'd drop the pitch or somebody'd muff the throw.
If he hit a pop fly the sun'd get in somebody's eyes. If
he took a swell third strike with the bases full the umps
would call it a ball. If he cut first base by twenty feet
the umps would be readin' the mornin' paper.

Zimmerman's leg mended, so that he was all right by
June; and then Saier got sick and they tried Speed at
first base. He'd never saw the bag before; but things
kept on breakin' for him and he played it like a house
afire. The Cubs copped the pennant and Speed got in
on the big dough, besides playin' a whale of a game
through the whole serious.

Speed and me both went back to Ishpeming to spend
the winter—though the Lord knows it ain't no winter

resort. Our homes was there; and besides, in my case, they was a certain girl livin' in the old burg.

Parker, o' course, was the hero and the swell guy when we got home. He'd been in the World's Serious and had plenty o' dough in his kick. I come home with nothin' but my suitcase and a hard-luck story, which I kept to myself. I hadn't even went good enough in Indianapolis to be sure of a job there again.

That fall—last fall—an uncle o' Speed's died over in the Soo and left him ten thousand bucks. I had an uncle down in the Lower Peninsula who was worth five times that much—but he had good health!

This girl I spoke about was the prettiest thing I ever see. I'd went with her in the old days, and when I blew back I found she was still strong for me. They wasn't a great deal o' variety in Ishpeming for a girl to pick from. Her and I went to the dance every Saturday night and to church Sunday nights. I called on her Wednesday evenin's, besides takin' her to all the shows that come along—rotten as the most o' them was.

I never knowed Speed was makin' a play for this doll till along last Feb'uary. The minute I seen what was up I got busy. I took her out sleigh-ridin' and kept her out in the cold till she'd promised to marry me. We set the date for this fall—I figured I'd know better where I was at by that time.

Well, we didn't make no secret o' bein' engaged; down in the poolroom one night Speed come up and congratulated me. He says:

"You got a swell girl, Dick! I wouldn't mind bein'

in your place. You're mighty lucky to cop her out—
you old Horseshoes, you!"

"Horseshoes!" I says. "You got a fine license to call
anybody Horseshoes!  I suppose you ain't never had
no luck?"

"Not like you," he says.

I was feelin' too good about grabbin' the girl to get
sore at the time; but when I got to thinkin' about it a
few minutes afterward it made me mad clear through.
What right did that bird have to talk about me bein'
lucky?

Speed was playin' freeze-out at a table near the door,
and when I started home some o' the boys with him
says:

"Good night, Dick."

I said good night and then Speed looked up.

"Good night, Horseshoes!" he says.

That got my nanny this time.

"Shut up, you lucky stiff!" I says. "If you wasn't so
dam' lucky you'd be sweepin' the streets." Then I
walks on out.

I was too busy with the girl to see much o' Speed
after that. He left home about the middle o' the month
to go to Tampa with the Cubs. I got notice from
Indianapolis that I was sold to Baltimore. I didn't care
much about goin' there and I wasn't anxious to leave
home under the circumstances, so I didn't report till late.

When I read in the papers along in April that Speed
had been traded to Boston for a couple o' pitchers I
thought: "Gee!  He must of lost his rabbit's foot!" Because, even if the Cubs didn't cop again, they'd have

a city serious with the White Sox and get a bunch o'
dough that way. And they wasn't no chance in the
world for the Boston Club to get nothin' but their
salaries.

It wasn't another month, though, till Shafer, o' the
Giants, quit baseball and McGraw was up against it for
a third baseman. Next thing I knowed Speed was traded
to New York and was with another winner—for they
never was out o' first place all season.

I was gettin' along all right at Baltimore and Dunnie
liked me; so I felt like I had somethin' more than just
a one-year job—somethin' I could get married on. It
was all framed that the weddin' was comin' off as soon
as this season was over; so you can believe I was pullin'
for October to hurry up and come.

One day in August, two months ago, Dunnie come in
the clubhouse and handed me the news.

"Rube Oldring's busted his leg," he says, "and he's
out for the rest o' the season. Connie's got a youngster
named Joyce that he can stick in there, but he's got
to have an extra outfielder. He's made me a good prop-
osition for you and I'm goin' to let you go. It'll be
pretty soft for you, because they got the pennant
cinched and they'll cut you in on the big money."

"Yes," I says; "and when they're through with me
they'll ship me to Hellangone, and I'll be draggin' down
about seventy-five bucks a month next year."

"Nothin' like that," says Dunnie. "If he don't want
you next season he's got to ask for waivers; and if you
get out o' the big league you come right back here.
That's all framed."

So that's how I come to get with the Ath-a-letics. Connie give me a nice, comf'table seat in one corner o' the bench and I had the pleasure o' watchin' a real ball club perform once every afternoon and sometimes twice.

Connie told me that as soon as they had the flag cinched he was goin' to lay off some o' his regulars and I'd get a chance to play.

Well, they cinched it the fourth day o' September and our next engagement was with Washin'ton on Labor Day. We had two games and I was in both of 'em. And I broke in with my usual lovely luck, because the pitchers I was ast to face was Boehling, a nasty left-hander, and this guy Johnson.

The mornin' game was Boehling and he wasn't no worse than some o' the rest of his kind. I only whiffed once and would of had a triple if Milan hadn't run from here to New Orleans and stole one off me.

I'm not boastin' about my first experience with Johnson though. They can't never tell me he throws them balls with his arm. He's got a gun concealed about his person and he shoots 'em up there. I was leadin' off in Murphy's place and the game was a little delayed in startin', because I'd watched the big guy warm up and wasn't in no hurry to get to that plate. Before I left the bench Connie says:

"Don't try to take no healthy swing. Just meet 'em and you'll get along better."

So I tried to just meet the first one he throwed; but when I stuck out my bat Henry was throwin' the pill back to Johnson. Then I thought: Maybe if I start swingin' now at the second one I'll hit the third one. So I let the second one come over and the umps guessed it was another strike, though I'll bet a thousand bucks he couldn't see it no more'n I could.

While Johnson was still windin' up to pitch again I started to swing—and the big cuss crosses me with a slow one. I lunged at it twice and missed it both times, and the force o' my wallop throwed me clean back to the bench. The Ath-a-letics was all laughin' at me and I laughed too, because I was glad that much of it was over.

McInnes gets a base hit off him in the second innin' and I ast him how he done it.

"He's a friend o' mine," says Jack, "and he lets up when he pitches to me."

I made up my mind right there that if I was goin' to be in the league next year I'd go out and visit Johnson this winter and get acquainted.

I wished before the day was over that I was hittin' in the catcher's place, because the fellers down near the tail-end of the battin' order only had to face him three times. He fanned me on three pitched balls again in the third, and when I come up in the sixth he scared me to death by pretty near beanin' me with the first one.

"Be careful!" says Henry. "He's gettin' pretty wild and he's liable to knock you away from your uniform."

"Don't he never curve one?" I ast.

"Sure!" says Henry. "Do you want to see his curve?"

"Yes," I says, knowin' the hook couldn't be no worse'n the fast one.

So he give me three hooks in succession and I missed 'em all; but I felt more comf'table than when I was duckin' his fast ball. In the ninth he hit my bat with a curve and the ball went on the ground to McBride. He booted it, but throwed me out easy—because I was so surprised at not havin' whiffed that I forgot to run!

Well, I went along like that for the rest o' the season, runnin' up against the best pitchers in the league and not exactly murderin' 'em. Everything I tried went wrong, and I was smart enough to know that if anything had depended on the games I wouldn't of been in there for two minutes. Joyce and Strunk and Murphy wasn't jealous o' me a bit; but they was glad to take turns restin', and I didn't care much how I went so long as I was sure of a job next year.

I'd wrote to the girl a couple o' times askin' her to set the exact date for our weddin'; but she hadn't paid no attention. She said she was glad I was with the Ath-a-letics, but she thought the Giants was goin' to beat us. I might of suspected from that that somethin' was wrong, because not even a girl would pick the Giants to trim that bunch of ourn. Finally, the day before the serious started, I sent her a kind o' sassy letter sayin' I guessed it was up to me to name the day, and askin' whether October twentieth was all right. I told her to wire me yes or no.

I'd been readin' the dope about Speed all season, and I knowed he'd had a whale of a year and that his luck was right with him; but I never dreamed a man could have the Lord on his side as strong as Speed did in that

World's Serious! I might as well tell you all the dope, so long as you wasn't there.

The first game was on our grounds and Connie give us a talkin' to in the clubhouse beforehand.

"The shorter this serious is," he says, "the better for us. If it's a long serious we're goin' to have trouble, because McGraw's got five pitchers he can work and we've got about three; so I want you boys to go at 'em from the jump and play 'em off their feet. Don't take things easy, because it ain't goin' to be no snap. Just because we've licked 'em before ain't no sign we'll do it this time."

Then he calls me to one side and ast me what I knowed about Parker.

"You was with the Cubs when he was, wasn't you?" he says.

"Yes," I says; "and he's the luckiest stiff you ever seen! If he got stewed and fell in the gutter he'd catch a fish."

"I don't like to hear a good ball player called lucky," says Connie. "He must have a lot of ability or McGraw wouldn't use him regular. And he's been hittin' about .340 and played a bang-up game at third base. That can't be all luck."

"Wait till you see him," I says; "and if you don't say he's the luckiest guy in the world you can sell me to the Boston Bloomer Girls. He's so lucky," I says, "that if they traded him to the St. Louis Browns they'd have the pennant cinched by the Fourth of July."

And I'll bet Connie was willin' to agree with me before it was over.

Well, the Chief worked against the Big Rube in that game. We beat 'em, but they give us a battle and it was Parker that made it close. We'd gone along nothin' and nothin' till the seventh, and then Rube walks Collins and Baker lifts one over that little old wall. You'd think by this time them New York pitchers would know better than to give that guy anything he can hit.

In their part o' the ninth the Chief still had 'em shut out and two down, and the crowd was goin' home; but Doyle gets hit in the sleeve with a pitched ball and it's Speed's turn. He hits a foul pretty near straight up, but Schang misjudges it. Then he lifts another one and this time McInnes drops it. He'd ought to of been out twice. The Chief tries to make him hit at a bad one then, because he'd got him two strikes and nothin'. He hit at it all right—kissed it for three bases between Strunk and Joyce! And it was a wild pitch that he hit. Doyle scores, o' course, and the bugs suddenly decide not to go home just yet. I fully expected to see him steal home and get away with it, but Murray cut into the first ball and lined out to Barry.

Plank beat Matty two to one the next day in New York, and again Speed and his rabbit's foot give us an awful argument. Matty wasn't so good as usual and we really ought to of beat him bad. Two different times Strunk was on second waitin' for any kind o' wallop, and both times Barry cracked 'em down the third-base line like a shot. Speed stopped the first one with his stomach and extricated the pill just in time to nail Barry at first base and retire the side. The next time he throwed his glove in front of his face in self-defense and the ball stuck in it.

In the sixth innin' Schang was on third base and Plank on first, and two down, and Murphy combed an awful one to Speed's left. He didn't have time to stoop over and he just stuck out his foot. The ball hit it and caromed in two hops right into Doyle's hands on second base before Plank got there. Then in the seventh Speed bunts one and Baker trips and falls goin' after it or he'd of threw him out a mile. They was two gone; so Speed steals second, and, o' course, Schang has to make a bad peg right at that time and lets him go to third. Then Collins boots one on Murray and they've got a run. But it didn't do 'em no good, because Collins and Baker and McInnes come up in the ninth and walloped 'em where Parker couldn't reach 'em.

Comin' back to Philly on the train that night, I says to Connie:

."What do you think o' that Parker bird now?"

"He's lucky, all right," says Connie smilin'; "but we won't hold it against him if he don't beat us with it."

"It ain't too late," I says. "He ain't pulled his real stuff yet."

The whole bunch was talkin' about him and his luck, and sayin' it was about time for things to break against him. I warned 'em that they wasn't no chance—that it was permanent with him.

Bush and Tesreau hooked up next day and neither o' them had much stuff. Everybody was hittin' and it looked like anybody's game right up to the ninth. Speed had got on every time he come up—the wind blowin' his fly balls away from the outfielders and the infielders bootin' when he hit 'em on the ground.

When the ninth started the score was seven apiece. Connie and McGraw both had their whole pitchin' staffs warmin' up. The crowd was wild, because they'd been all kinds of action. They wasn't no danger of anybody's leavin' their seats before this game was over.

Well, Bescher is walked to start with and Connie's about ready to give Bush the hook; but Doyle pops out tryin' to bunt. Then Speed gets two strikes and two balls, and it looked to me like the next one was right over the heart; but Connolly calls it a ball and gives him another chance. He whales the groove ball to the fence in left center and gets round to third on it, while Bescher scores. Right then Bush comes out and the Chief goes in. He whiffs Murray and has two strikes on Merkle when Speed makes a break for home—and, o' course, that was the one ball Schang dropped in the whole serious!

They had a two-run lead on us then and it looked like a cinch for them to hold it, because the minute Tesreau showed a sign o' weakenin' McGraw was sure to holler for Matty or the Rube. But you know how quick that bunch of ourn can make a two-run lead look sick. Before McGraw could get Jeff out o' there we had two on the bases.

Then Rube comes in and fills 'em up by walkin' Joyce. It was Eddie's turn to wallop and if he didn't do nothin' we had Baker comin' up next. This time Collins saved Baker the trouble and whanged one clear to the woods. Everybody scored but him—and he could of, too, if it'd been necessary.

In the clubhouse the boys naturally felt pretty good. We'd copped three in a row and it looked like we'd make it four straight, because we had the Chief to send back at 'em the followin' day.

"Your friend Parker is lucky," the boys says to me, "but it don't look like he could stop us now."

I felt the same way and was consultin' the time-tables to see whether I could get a train out o' New York for the West next evenin'. But do you think Speed's luck was ready to quit? Not yet! And it's a wonder we didn't all go nuts durin' the next few days. If words could kill, Speed would of died a thousand times. And I wish he had!

They wasn't no record-breakin' crowd out when we got to the Polo Grounds. I guess the New York bugs was pretty well discouraged and the bettin' was eight to five that we'd cop that battle and finish it. The Chief was the only guy that warmed up for us and McGraw didn't have no choice but to use Matty, with the whole thing dependin' on this game.

They went along like the two swell pitchers they was till Speed's innin', which in this battle was the eighth. Nobody scored, and it didn't look like they was ever goin' to till Murphy starts off that round with a perfect bunt and Joyce sacrifices him to second. All Matty had to do then was to get rid o' Collins and Baker—and that's about as easy as sellin' silk socks to an Eskimo.

He didn't give Eddie nothin' he wanted to hit, though; and finally he slaps one on the ground to Doyle.

Larry made the play to first base and Murphy moved to third. We all figured Matty'd walk Baker then, and he done it. Connie sends Baker down to second on the first pitch to McInnes, but Meyers don't pay no attention to him—they was playin' for McInnes and wasn't takin' no chances o' throwin' the ball away.

Well, the count goes to three and two on McInnes and Matty comes with a curve—he's got some curve too; but Jack happened to meet it and—Blooie! Down the left foul line where he always hits! I never seen a ball hit so hard in my life. No infielder in the world could of stopped it. But I'll give you a thousand bucks if that ball didn't go kerplunk right into the third bag and stop as dead as George Washington! It was child's play for Speed to pick it up and heave it over to Merkle before Jack got there. If anybody else had been playin' third base the bag would of ducked out o' the way o' that wallop; but even the bases themselves was helpin' him out.

The two runs we ought to of had on Jack's smash would of been just enough to beat 'em, because they got the only run o' the game in their half—or, I should say, the Lord give it to 'em.

Doyle'd been throwed out and up come Parker, smilin'. The minute I seen him smile I felt like somethin' was comin' off and I made the remark on the bench.

Well, the Chief pitched one right at him and he tried to duck. The ball hit his bat and went on a line between Jack and Eddie. Speed didn't know he'd hit it till the guys on the bench wised him up. Then he just had time to get to first base. They tried the hit-and-run on

the second ball and Murray lifts a high fly that Murphy
didn't have to move for. Collins pulled the old bluff
about the ball bein' on the ground and Barry yells, "Go
on! Go on!" like he was the coacher. Speed fell for
it and didn't know where the ball was no more'n a
rabbit; he just run his fool head off and we was gettin'
all ready to laugh when the ball come down and
Murphy dropped it!

If Parker had stuck near first base, like he ought to
of done, he couldn't of got no farther'n second; but
with the start he got he was pretty near third when
Murphy made the muff, and it was a cinch for him to
score. The next two guys was easy outs; so they
wouldn't of had a run except for Speed's boner. We
couldn't do nothin' in the ninth and we was licked.

Well, that was a tough one to lose; but we figured
that Matty was through and we'd wind it up the next
day, as we had Plank ready to send back at 'em. We
wasn't afraid o' the Rube, because he hadn't never
bothered Collins and Baker much.

The two lefthanders come together just like everybody's doped it and it was about even up to the eighth.
Plank had been goin' great and, though the score was
two and two, they'd got their two on boots and we'd
hit ourn in. We went after Rube in our part o' the
eighth and knocked him out. Demaree stopped us after
we'd scored two more.

"It's all over but the shoutin';" says Davis on the
bench.

"Yes," I says, "unless that seventh son of a seventh
son gets up there again."

He did, and he come up after they'd filled the bases with a boot, a base hit and a walk with two out. I says to Davis:

"If I was Plank I'd pass him and give 'em one run."

"That wouldn't be no baseball," says Davis—"not with Murray comin' up."

Well, it mayn't of been no baseball, but it couldn't of turned out worse if they'd did it that way. Speed took a healthy at the first ball; but it was a hook and he caught it on the handle, right up near his hands. It started outside the first-base line like a foul and then changed its mind and rolled in. Schang run away from the plate, because it looked like it was up to him to make the play. He picked the ball up and had to make the peg in a hurry.

His throw hit Speed right on top o' the head and bounded off like it had struck a cement sidewalk. It went clear over to the seats and before McInnes could get it three guys had scored and Speed was on third base. He was left there, but that didn't make no difference. We was licked again and for the first time the gang really begun to get scared.

We went over to New York Sunday afternoon and we didn't do no singin' on the way. Some o' the fellers tried to laugh, but it hurt 'em. Connie sent us to bed early, but I don't believe none o' the bunch got much sleep—I know I didn't; I was worryin' too much about the serious and also about the girl, who hadn't sent me no telegram like I'd ast her to. Monday mornin' I wired her askin' what was the matter and tellin' her I was gettin' tired of her foolishness. O' course I didn't make it so strong as that—but the telegram cost me a dollar and forty cents.

Connie had the choice o' two pitchers for the sixth game. He could use Bush, who'd been slammed round pretty hard last time out, or the Chief, who'd only had two days' rest. The rest of 'em—outside o' Plank—had a epidemic o' sore arms. Connie finally picked Bush, so's he could have the Chief in reserve in case we had to play a seventh game. McGraw started Big Jeff and we went at it.

It wasn't like the last time these two guys had hooked up. This time they both had somethin', and for eight innin's runs was as scarce as Chinese policemen. They'd been chances to score on both sides, but the big guy and Bush was both tight in the pinches. The crowd was plumb nuts and yelled like Indians every time a fly ball was caught or a strike called. They'd of got their money's worth if they hadn't been no ninth; but, believe me, that was some round!

They was one out when Barry hit one through the box for a base. Schang walked, and it was Bush's turn. Connie told him to bunt, but he whiffed in the attempt. Then Murphy comes up and walks—and the bases are choked. Young Joyce had been pie for Tesreau all day or else McGraw might of changed pitchers right there. Anyway he left Big Jeff in and he beaned Joyce with a fast one. It sounded like a tire blowin' out. Joyce falls over in a heap and we chase out there, thinkin' he's dead; but he ain't, and pretty soon he gets up and walks down to first base. Tesreau had forced in a run and again we begun to count the winner's end. Matty comes

in to prevent further damage and Collins flies the side
out.

"Hold 'em now! Work hard!" we says to young
Bush, and he walks out there just as cool as though he
was goin' to hit fungoes.

McGraw sends up a pinch hitter for Matty and Bush
whiffed him. Then Bescher flied out. I was prayin'
that Doyle would end it, because Speed's turn come
after his'n; so I pretty near fell dead when Larry hit
safe.

Speed had his old smile and even more chest than
usual when he come up there, swingin' five or six bats.
He didn't wait for Doyle to try and steal, or nothin'.
He lit into the first ball, though Bush was tryin' to
waste it. I seen the ball go high in the air toward left
field, and then I picked up my glove and got ready to
beat it for the gate. But when I looked out to see if
Joyce was set, what do you think I seen? He was lyin'
flat on the ground! That blow on the head had got him
just as Bush was pitchin' to Speed. He'd flopped over
and didn't no more know what was goin' on than if
he'd croaked.

Well, everybody else seen it at the same time; but it
was too late. Strunk made a run for the ball, but they
wasn't no chance for him to get near it. It hit the
ground about ten feet back o' where Joyce was lyin'
and bounded way over to the end o' the foul line. You
don't have to be told that Doyle and Parker both scored
and the serious was tied up.

We carried Joyce to the clubhouse and after a while
he come to. He cried when he found out what had

happened. We cheered him up all we could, but he was a pretty sick guy. The trainer said he'd be all right, though, for the final game.

They tossed up a coin to see where they'd play the seventh battle and our club won the toss; so we went back to Philly that night and cussed Parker clear across New Jersey. I was so sore I kicked the stuffin' out o' my seat.

You probably heard about the excitement in the burg yesterday mornin'. The demand for tickets was somethin' fierce and some of 'em sold for as high as twenty-five bucks apiece. Our club hadn't been lookin' for no seventh game and they was some tall hustlin' done round that old ball park.

I started out to the grounds early and bought some New York papers to read on the car. They was a big story that Speed Parker, the Giants' hero, was goin' to be married a week after the end o' the serious. It didn't give the name o' the girl, sayin' Speed had refused to tell it. I figured she must be some dame he'd met round the circuit somewheres.

They was another story by one o' them smart baseball reporters sayin' that Parker, on his way up to the plate, had saw that Joyce was about ready to faint and had hit the fly ball to left field on purpose. Can you beat it?

I was goin' to show that to the boys in the clubhouse, but the minute I blowed in there I got some news that made me forget about everything else. Joyce was very sick and they'd took him to a hospital. It was up to me to play!

Connie come over and ast me whether I'd ever hit against Matty. I told him I hadn't, but I'd saw enough of him to know he wasn't no worse'n Johnson. He told me he was goin' to let me hit second—in Joyce's place—because he didn't want to bust up the rest of his combination. He also told me to take my orders from Strunk about where to play for the batters.

"Where shall I play for Parker?" I says, tryin' to joke and pretend I wasn't scared to death.

"I wisht I could tell you," says Connie. "I guess the only thing to do when he comes up is to get down on your knees and pray."

The rest o' the bunch slapped me on the back and give me all the encouragement they could. The place was jammed when we went out on the field. They may of been bigger crowds before, but they never was packed together so tight. I doubt whether they was even room enough left for Falkenberg to sit down.

The afternoon papers had printed the stuff about Joyce bein' out of it, so the bugs was wise that I was goin' to play. They watched me pretty close in battin' practice and give me a hand whenever I managed to hit one hard. When I was out catchin' fungoes the guys in the bleachers cheered me and told me they was with me; but I don't mind tellin' you that I was as nervous as a bride.

They wasn't no need for the announcers to tip the crowd off to the pitchers. Everybody in the United States and Cuba knowed that the Chief'd work for us and Matty for them. The Chief didn't have no trouble with 'em in the first innin'. Even from where I stood

I could see that he had a lot o' stuff. Bescher and Doyle popped out and Speed whiffed.

Well, I started out makin' good, with reverse English, in our part. Fletcher booted Murphy's ground ball and I was sent up to sacrifice. I done a complete job of it—sacrificin' not only myself but Murphy with a pop fly that Matty didn't have to move for. That spoiled whatever chance we had o' gettin' the jump on 'em; but the boys didn't bawl me for it.

"That's all right, old boy. You're all right!" they said on the bench—if they'd had a gun they'd of shot me.

I didn't drop no fly balls in the first six innin's—because none was hit out my way. The Chief was so good that they wasn't hittin' nothin' out o' the infield. And we wasn't doin' nothin' with Matty, either. I led off in the fourth and fouled the first one. I didn't molest the other two. But if Connie and the gang talked about me they done it internally. I come up again—with Murphy on third base and two gone in the sixth, and done my little whiffin' specialty. And still the only people that panned me was the thirty thousand that had paid for the privilege!

My first fieldin' chance come in the seventh. You'd of thought that I'd of had my nerve back by that time; but I was just as scared as though I'd never saw a crowd before. It was just as well that they was two out when Merkle hit one to me. I staggered under it and finally it hit me on the shoulder. Merkle got to second, but the Chief whiffed the next guy. I was gave some cross looks on the bench and I shouldn't of blamed the fellers if they'd cut loose with some language; but they didn't.

They's no use in me tellin' you about none o' the rest of it—except what happened just before the start o' the eleventh and durin' that innin', which was sure the big one o' yesterday's pastime—both for Speed and yours sincerely.

The scoreboard was still a row o' ciphers and Speed'd had only a fair amount o' luck. He'd made a scratch base hit and robbed our bunch of a couple o' real ones with impossible stops.

When Schang flied out and wound up our tenth I was leanin' against the end of our bench. I heard my name spoke, and I turned round and seen a boy at the door.

"Right here!" I says; and he give me a telegram.

"Better not open it till after the game," says Connie.

"Oh, no; it ain't no bad news," I said, for I figured it was an answer from the girl. So I opened it up and read it on the way to my position. It said:

"Forgive me, Dick—and forgive Speed too. Letter follows."

Well, sir, I ain't no baby, but for a minute I just wanted to sit down and bawl. And then, all of a sudden, I got so mad I couldn't see. I run right into Baker as he was pickin' up his glove. Then I give him a shove and called him some name, and him and Barry both looked at me like I was crazy—and I was. When I got out in left field I stepped on my own foot and spiked it. I just had to hurt somebody.

As I remember it the Chief fanned the first two of 'em. Then Doyle catches one just right and lams it up against the fence back o' Murphy. The ball caromed round some and Doyle got all the way to third base. Next thing I seen was Speed struttin' up to the plate. I run clear in from my position.

"Kill him!" I says to the Chief. "Hit him in the head and kill him, and I'll go to jail for it!"

"Are you off your nut?" says the Chief. "Go out there and play ball—and quit ravin'."

Barry and Baker led me away and give me a shove out toward left. Then I heard the crack o' the bat and I seen the ball comin' a mile a minute. It was headed between Strunk and I and looked like it would go out o' the park. I don't remember runnin' or nothin' about it till I run into the concrete wall head first. They told me afterward and all the papers said that it was the greatest catch ever seen. And I never knowed I'd caught the ball!

Some o' the managers have said my head was pretty hard, but it wasn't as hard as that concrete. I was pretty near out, but they tell me I walked to the bench like I wasn't hurt at all. They also tell me that the crowd was a bunch o' ravin' maniacs and was throwin' money at me. I guess the ground-keeper'll get it.

The boys on the bench was all talkin' at once and slappin' me on the back, but I didn't know what it was about. Somebody told me pretty soon that it was my turn to hit and I picked up the first bat I come to and starts for the plate. McInnes come runnin' after me and ast me whether I didn't want my own bat. I cussed him and told him to mind his own business.

I didn't know it at the time, but I found out afterward

that they was two out. The bases was empty. I'll tell
you just what I had in my mind: I wasn't thinkin' about
the ball game; I was determined that I was goin' to get
to third base and give that guy my spikes. If I didn't
hit one worth three bases, or if I didn't hit one at all,
I was goin' to run till I got round to where Speed was,
and then slide into him and cut him to pieces!

Right now I can't tell you whether I hit a fast ball,
or a slow ball, or a hook, or a fader—but I hit somethin'.
It went over Bescher's head like a shot and then took
a crazy bound. It must of struck a rock or a pop bottle,
because it hopped clear over the fence and landed in
the bleachers.

Mind you, I learned this afterward. At the time I
just knowed I'd hit one somewheres and I starts round
the bases. I speeded up when I got near third and took
a runnin' jump at a guy I thought was Parker. I missed
him and sprawled all over the bag. Then, all of a sudden, I come to my senses. All the Ath-a-letics was out
there to run home with me and it was one o' them I'd
tried to cut. Speed had left the field. The boys picked
me up and seen to it that I went on and touched the
plate. Then I was carried into the clubhouse by the
crazy bugs.

Well, they had a celebration in there and it was a
long time before I got a chance to change my clothes.
The boys made a big fuss over me. They told me they'd
intended to give me five hundred bucks for my divvy,
but now I was goin' to get a full share.

"Parker ain't the only lucky guy!" says one of 'em.

"But even if that ball hadn't of took that crazy hop you'd of had a triple."

A triple! That's just what I'd wanted; and he called me lucky for not gettin' it!

The Giants was dressin' in the other part o' the club-house; and when I finally come out there was Speed, standin' waitin' for some o' the others. He seen me comin' and he smiled. "Hello, Horseshoes!" he says.

He won't smile no more for a while—it'll hurt too much. And if any girl wants him when she sees him now—with his nose over shakin' hands with his ear, and his jaw a couple o' feet foul—she's welcome to him. They won't be no contest!

Grimes leaned over to ring for the waiter.

"Well," he said, "what about it?"

"You won't have to pay my fare," I told him.

"I'll buy a drink anyway," said he. "You've been a good listener—and I had to get it off my chest."

"Maybe they'll have to postpone the wedding," I said.

"No," said Grimes. "The weddin' will take place the day after tomorrow—and I'll bat for Mr. Parker. Did you think I was goin' to let him get away with it?"

"What about next year?" I asked.

"I'm goin' back to the Ath-a-letics," he said. "And I'm goin' to hire somebody to call me 'Horseshoes!' before every game—because I can sure play that old baseball when I'm mad."

# MY FINANCIAL CAREER by Stephen Leacock

WHEN I go into a bank I get rattled. The clerks rattle me; the wickets rattle me; the sight of the money rattles me; everything rattles me.

The moment I cross the threshold of a bank and attempt to transact business there, I become an irresponsible idiot.

I knew this beforehand, but my salary had been raised to fifty dollars a month and I felt that the bank was the only place for it.

So I shambled in and looked timidly round at the clerks. I had an idea that a person about to open an account must needs consult the manager.

I went up to a wicket marked "Accountant." The accountant was a tall, cool devil. The very sight of him rattled me. My voice was sepulchral.

"Can I see the manager?" I said, and added solemnly, "alone." I don't know why I said "alone."

"Certainly," said the accountant, and fetched him.

The manager was a grave, calm man. I held my fifty-six dollars clutched in a crumpled ball in my pocket.

"Are you the manager?" I said. God knows I didn't doubt it.

"Yes," he said.

"Can I see you," I asked, "alone?" I didn't want to say "alone" again, but without it the thing seemed self-evident.

The manager looked at me in some alarm. He felt that I had an awful secret to reveal.

"Come in here," he said, and led the way to a private room. He turned the key in the lock.

"We are safe from interruption here," he said; "sit down."

We both sat down and looked at each other. I found no voice to speak.

"You are one of Pinkerton's men, I presume," he said.

He had gathered from my mysterious manner that I was a detective. I knew what he was thinking, and it made me worse.

"No, not from Pinkerton's," I said, seeming to imply that I came from a rival agency.

"To tell the truth," I went on, as if I had been prompted to lie about it, "I am not a detective at all. I have come to open an account. I intend to keep all my money in this bank."

The manager looked relieved but still serious; he concluded now that I was a son of Baron Rothschild or a young Gould.

"A large account, I suppose," he said.

"Fairly large," I whispered. "I propose to deposit fifty-six dollars now and fifty dollars a month regularly."

The manager got up and opened the door. He called to the accountant.

"Mr. Montgomery," he said unkindly loud, "this gentleman is opening an account, he will deposit fifty-six dollars. Good morning."

I rose.

A big iron door stood open at the side of the room. "Good morning," I said, and stepped into the safe.

"Come out," said the manager coldly, and showed me the other way.

I went up to the accountant's wicket and poked the ball of money at him with a quick convulsive movement as if I were doing a conjuring trick.

My face was ghastly pale.

"Here," I said, "deposit it." The tone of the words seemed to mean, "Let us do this painful thing while the fit is on us."

He took the money and gave it to another clerk.

He made me write the sum on a slip and sign my name in a book. I no longer knew what I was doing. The bank swam before my eyes.

"Is it deposited?" I asked in a hollow, vibrating voice.

"It is," said the accountant.

"Then I want to draw a cheque."

My idea was to draw out six dollars of it for present use. Someone gave me a cheque-book through a wicket and someone else began telling me how to write it out. The people in the bank had the impression that I was an invalid millionaire. I wrote something on the cheque and thrust it in at the clerk. He looked at it.

"What! are you drawing it all out again?" he asked in surprise. Then I realised that I had written fifty-six instead of six. I was too far gone to reason now. I had a feeling that it was impossible to explain the thing. All the clerks had stopped writing to look at me.

Reckless with misery, I made a plunge.

"Yes, the whole thing."

"You withdraw your money from the bank?"

"Every cent of it."

"Are you not going to deposit any more?" said the clerk, astonished.

"Never."

An idiot hope struck me that they might think something had insulted me while I was writing the cheque and that I had changed my mind. I made a wretched attempt to look like a man with a fearfully quick temper.

The clerk prepared to pay the money.

"How will you have it?" he said.

"What?"

"How will you have it?"

"Oh"—I caught his meaning and answered without even trying to think—"in fifties."

He gave me a fifty-dollar bill.

"And the six?" he asked dryly.

"In sixes," I said.

He gave it me and I rushed out.

As the big door swung behind me I caught the echo of a roar of laughter that went up to the ceiling of the bank. Since then I bank no more. I keep my money in cash in my trousers pocket and my savings in silver dollars in a sock.

## STRANGER IN THE HOUSE by Ogden Nash

MR. PERKINS was a diffident young man, awkward
enough among his own friends in Boston; the prospect
of presenting himself to friends of friends below the
Mason and Dixon line was a discomposing one. However, he had promised before leaving home that he
would look up Mrs. Ambrose and her mother, so now
he sat fidgeting in the taxi as the meter ticked him ever
closer to tea with strangers. He had no idea where he
was. The streets of the residential district not only
writhed and twisted; occasionally they disappeared into
each other, like a snake swallowing its tail. Without
warning, what had been Mulberry Road was suddenly
Pinegrove Road, which, after crossing Middlesex Drive,
continued as Oak Lane.

"What's that number again?" asked the driver.

"Nineteen," said Mr. Perkins. He looked out the
window. "Thirteen, fifteen, seventeen, here we are—
No, we've passed it, this is twenty-one."

"Take it easy," said the driver. "Nineteen's right
beyond twenty-five. Don't ask me why," he said as the
cab stopped. "Oak Lane runs twenty-three, twenty-

five, nineteen, and that's all I know. They say," he added inconsistently, "nineteen was here first."

Mr. Perkins walked up the path, rang the bell of a pleasant Georgian house, was admitted by a maid, and, a moment later, stood hesitantly in the doorway of a fairly populous drawing room.

"Mr. Perkle, Ma'am," said the maid, and disappeared.

A pretty woman in her early forties came toward him. "Do come in, Mr. Perkins. I'm Louise Ambrose. This is Mr. Perkins, Mother, he's a great friend of the Bemises in Boston. And my aunt, Mrs. Hammond, and my father, Mr. Strong, Mr. Perkins."

"How do you do," murmured Mr. Perkins. "It's very kind of you to take me in."

"Bemis, Bemis," said Mrs. Strong. "Which Bemises, Louise—the Crafton Bemises?"

"No, Mother, the Harry Bemises. The Crafton Bemises live in St. Louis, don't you remember?"

"I thought the Crafton Bemises lived in Chicago," said Mrs. Hammond. "It's the de Graffs who live in St. Louis."

"Well, Mr. Perkins is a friend of the *Harry* Bemises, Aunt Charlotte, and they live in Boston. May I give you some tea, Mr. Perkins?"

"There was a Bemis in my company at Plattsburg," said Mr. Strong. "Bob Bemis, or maybe Frank. I know he went either to Harvard or M.I.T."

"How are the Bemises, Mr. Perkins?" asked Mrs. Ambrose.

"In pretty bad shape, I'm afraid. They were driving out to Newburyport, and this big truck—"

"Dudley says the Newburyport Pike is a deathtrap," said Mrs. Hammond.

"Big Dudley or Little Dudley?" asked Mrs. Strong.

"Oh, Big Dudley," said Mrs. Hammond. "The time he had the blowout in Ipswich."

"Big Dudley is my uncle," explained Mrs. Ambrose. "Little Dudley is my cousin. Little Dudley is four inches taller than Big Dudley, so it's rather confusing. Tea, Mr. Perkins?"

"I don't see why," said Mrs. Strong. "When Little Dudley was little he was littler."

"It wasn't Bemis at all," said Mr. Strong. "It was Beebe, Albert Beebe. He went to Lehigh."

"They were only doing about forty," said Mr. Perkins, "but this truck came over the hill—"

"Sarah Susan says the trucks are ruining the railroads," said Mrs. Strong.

"Big Sarah Susan or Little Sarah Susan?" asked Mrs. Hammond.

"Little Sarah Susan," said Mrs. Strong. "You know that Pennsylvania stock Henry gave her."

"Big Sarah Susan is another aunt," explained Mrs. Ambrose. "Little Sarah Susan is her daughter. How do you take it, Mr. Perkins?"

"They're both the same size now," said Mrs. Strong, "but Big Sarah Susan and Little Sarah Susan sounds better than Young Sarah Susan and Old Sarah Susan."

"Big Sarah Susan isn't so old," said Mrs. Hammond. "Not more than fifty-three."

"Oh, I think she's a bit older than that," said Mrs. Strong. "When was Little Sarah Susan born?"

"Ninteen-twenty," said Mrs. Hammond.

"Nineteen-nineteen, wasn't it?" said Mrs. Strong.

"Nineteen-twenty," repeated Mrs. Hammond firmly. "I remember distinctly that the telephone rang while Little Dudley was asking Big Dudley if he could watch Henry kill the hog, and it was Henry to say that Sarah Susan had a little girl, and we killed our last hog in nineteen-twenty."

"The one who telephoned was *Uncle* Henry," explained Mrs. Ambrose. "The one who killed the hog was Colored Henry."

"Charlotte, you killed that hog in nineteen-nineteen," said Mrs. Strong. "You sent us sausages, and Aunt Tansy took it into her head to boil them, and that was the first sign she was losing her mind and the next week we had to pension her."

"Aunt Tansy was our cook," explained Mrs. Ambrose. "Did you say cream, Mr. Perkins?"

"Nineteen-twenty," said Mrs. Hammond.

"Nineteen-nineteen," said Mrs. Strong. "I can show you the stubs in my checkbook."

"They have a darned good engineering course at Lehigh," said Mr. Strong.

"Harry tried to cut back into line," said Mr. Perkins, "but the truck was coming too fast and—"

"Do you remember the time Gandy had the truck driver arrested for spitting into the Susquehanna?" asked Mrs. Strong. "She said it tainted the shad roe."

"I certainly do," said Mrs. Hammond. "Gamma paid his fine."

"Gandy was my great-grandmother," explained Mrs.

Ambrose. "Gamma was my grandmother. Mother, Mr. Perkins hasn't had any tea."

"Gandy liked her shad roe without salt and pepper," said Mrs. Strong.

"So does Young Dudley," said Mrs. Hammond. "He's the only one in the family that takes after Gandy that way."

"Young Dudley is Little Dudley's boy," explained Mrs. Ambrose. "He's named after Big Dudley."

"I'd as soon have good herring roe as shad roe any day in the week," said Mr. Strong.

"Grace was only shaken up, but Harry had a broken leg and a concussion," said Mr. Perkins. "He'll be in the hospital about—"

"I nearly forgot the news!" cried Mrs. Hammond. "Little Dudley and Jane are having another baby."

"Isn't Jane a little old for that?" asked Mrs. Strong. "How old is she, Charlotte?"

"Let me think," said Mrs. Hammond. "Jane joined the dancing class the year Sarah Susan couldn't chaperone because she was having Little Sarah Susan, so she was thirteen in nineteen-twenty."

"Nineteen-nineteen, Charlotte," said Mrs. Strong. "I'll show you my old checkbook."

Mr. Perkins got up. "I'm afraid I must run along. My train—"

"Goodbye, Mr. Perkins. I wish you could stay for dinner with us," said Mrs. Ambrose.

"Give my love to the Bemises. I'm so glad to hear they're well," said Mrs. Hammond.

"Tell them I'll call them next time I'm in St. Louis," said Mrs. Strong. "Why, you didn't take any tea. Charles, why didn't you offer Mr. Perkins a highball?"

"By George," said Mr. Strong, "I haven't seen old Harry since Little Sarah Susan was born."

# FROU-FROU, OR THE FUTURE OF VERTIGO by S. J. Perelman

JUST in case anybody here missed me at the Mermaid Tavern this afternoon when the bowl of sack was being passed, I spent most of it reclining on my chaise longue in a negligee trimmed with maribou, reading trashy bonbons and eating French yellow-backed novels. What between amnesia (inability to find my rubbers) and total recall (ability to remember all the cunning things I did last night), you might think I'd have sense enough to sit still and mind my own business. But, oh, no—not I. *I* had to start looking through *Harper's Bazaar* yet.

If a perfectly strange lady came up to you on the street and demanded, "Why don't you travel with a little raspberry-colored cashmere blanket to throw over yourself in hotels and trains?" the chances are that you would turn on your heel with dignity and hit her with a bottle. Yet that is exactly what has been happening for the past twenty months in the pages of a little raspberry-colored magazine called *Harper's Bazaar*. And don't think it does any good to pretend there *is* no magazine called *Harper's Bazaar*. I've tried that, too,

and all I get is something called "circular insanity."
Imagine having both circular insanity and *Harper's
Bazaar!*

The first time I noticed this "Why Don't You?"
department was a year ago last August while hungrily
devouring news of the midsummer Paris openings.
Without any preamble came the stinging query, "Why
don't you rinse your blonde child's hair in dead champagne, as they do in France? Or pat her face gently
with cream before she goes to bed, as they do in England?" After a quick look into the nursery, I decided
to let my blonde child go to hell in her own way, as
they do in America, and read on. "Why don't you,"
continued the author, spitting on her hands, "twist her
pigtails around her ears like macaroons?" I reread this
several times to make sure I wasn't dreaming and then
turned to the statement of ownership in the back of the
magazine. Just because the Marquis de Sade wasn't
mentioned didn't fool *me*; you know as well as I do
who must have controlled fifty-one per cent of the
stock. I slept across the foot of the crib with a loaded
horse pistol until the next issue appeared.

It appeared, all right, all right, and after a quick
gander at the activities of Nicky de Gunzburg, Lady
Abdy, and the Vicomtesse de Noailles, which left me
right back where I started, I sought out my "Why
Don't You?" column. "Why don't you try the effect
of diamond roses and ribbons flat on your head, as
Garbo wears them when she says good-bye to Armand
in their country retreat?" asked Miss Sly Boots in a
low, thrilling voice. I was living in my own country

retreat at the time, and as it happened to be my day to go to the post office (ordinarily the post office comes to me), I welcomed this chance to vary the monotony. Piling my head high with diamond roses and ribbons, I pulled on a pair of my stoutest *espadrilles* and set off, my cat frisking ahead of me with many a warning cry of "Here comes my master, the Marquis of Carabas!" We reached the post office without incident, except for the elderly Amish woman hoeing cabbages in her garden. As I threw her a cheery greeting, Goody Two-shoes looked up, gave a rapid exhibition of Cheyne-Stokes breathing, and immediately turned to stone. In case you ever get down that way, she is still standing there, slightly chipped but otherwise in very good condition, which is more than I can say for the postmaster. When I walked in, he was in process of spitting into the top drawer, where he keeps the money-order blanks. One look at Boxholder 14 and he went out the window without bothering to raise the sash. A second later I heard a frightened voice directing a small boy to run for the hex doctor next door to the Riegels'. I spent the night behind some willows near the Delaware and managed to work my way back to the farm without being detected, but it was a matter of months before I was able to convince the countryside that I had a twin brother, enormously wealthy but quite mad, who had eluded his guards and paid me a visit.

For a time I went on a sort of *Harper's Bazaar* wagon, tapering myself off on *Pictorial Review* and *Good Housekeeping*, but deep down I knew I was a gone goose. Whenever I got too near a newsstand bearing a current issue of the *Bazaar* and my head started to swim, I would rush home and bury myself in dress patterns. And then, one inevitable day, the dam burst. Lingering in Brentano's basement over *L'Illustration* and *Blanco y Negro*, I felt the delicious, shuddery, half-swooning sensation of being drawn into the orbit again. On a table behind me lay a huge stack of the very latest issue of *Harper's Bazaar*, smoking hot from the presses. "Ah, come on," I heard my evil genius whisper. "One little peek can't hurt you. Nobody's looking." With trembling fingers I fumbled through the advertisements for Afghan hounds, foundation garments, and bath foams to the "Why Don't You?" section. Tiny beads of perspiration stood out on my even tinier forehead as I began to read, "Why don't you build beside the sea, or in the center of your garden, a white summer dining room shaped like a tent, draped with wooden swags, with walls of screen and Venetian blinds, so you will be safe from bugs and drafts?" I recoiled, clawing the air. "No, no!" I screamed. "I won't! I can't! *Help!*" But already the column was coiling around me, its hot breath on my neck. "Why don't you concentrate on fur jackets of marvelous workmanship and cut, made of inexpensive furs with incomprehensible names? Why don't you bring back from Central Europe a huge white baroque porcelain stove to stand in your front hall, reflected in the parquet? Why don't you buy in a hardware store a plain pine knife-basket with two compartments and a handle—mount this on four legs and you will have the ideal little table to sort letters and bills on, and to carry from your bedside to the garden or wherever you happen to be?" Unfortunately I had only the two legs God gave me, but I mounted those basement stairs like a cheetah, fought off the restraining hands of voluptuous salesladies, and hurtled out into the cool, sweet air of West Forty-seventh Street. I'm sorry I snatched the paper knife out of that desk set, Mr. Brentano, but you can send a boy around for it at my expense. And by the way, do you ever have any call for back numbers of fashion magazines?

# THE SCHARTZ–METTERKLUME METHOD by Saki

LADY CARLOTTA stepped out on to the platform of the small wayside station and took a turn or two up and down its uninteresting length, to kill time till the train should be pleased to proceed on its way. Then, in the roadway beyond, she saw a horse struggling with a more than ample load, and a carter of the sort that seems to bear a sullen hatred against the animal that helps him to earn a living. Lady Carlotta promptly betook her to the roadway, and put rather a different complexion on the struggle. Certain of her acquaintances were wont to give her plentiful admonition as to the undesirability of interfering on behalf of a distressed animal, such interference being "none of her business." Only once had she put the doctrine of non-interference into practice, when one of its most eloquent exponents had been besieged for nearly three hours in a small and extremely uncomfortable may-tree by an angry boar-pig, while Lady Carlotta, on the other side of the fence, had proceeded with the water-colour sketch she was engaged on, and refused to interfere between the boar and his prisoner. It is to be feared that she lost the friendship of the ultimately rescued lady. On this occasion she merely lost the train, which gave way to the first sign of impatience it had shown throughout the journey, and steamed off without her. She bore the desertion with philosophical indifference; her friends and relations were thoroughly well used to the fact of her luggage arriving without her. She wired a vague non-committal message to her destination to say that she was coming on "by another train." Before she had time to think what her next move might be she was confronted by an imposingly attired lady, who seemed to be taking a prolonged mental inventory of her clothes and looks.

"You must be Miss Hope, the governess I've come to meet," said the apparition, in a tone that admitted of very little argument.

"Very well, if I must I must," said Lady Carlotta to herself with dangerous meekness.

"I am Mrs. Quabarl," continued the lady; "and where, pray, is your luggage?"

"It's gone astray," said the alleged governess, falling in with the excellent rule of life that the absent are always to blame; the luggage had, in point of fact, behaved with perfect correctitude. "I've just telegraphed about it," she added, with a nearer approach to truth.

"How provoking," said Mrs. Quabarl; "these railway companies are so careless. However, my maid can lend you things for the night," and she led the way to her car.

During the drive to the Quabarl mansion Lady Carlotta was impressively introduced to the nature of the charge that had been thrust upon her; she learned that Claude and Wilfrid were delicate, sensitive young people, that Irene had the artistic temperament highly developed, and that Viola was something or other else of a mould equally commonplace among children of that class and type in the twentieth century.

"I wish them not only to be *taught*," said Mrs. Quabarl, "but *interested* in what they learn. In their history lessons, for instance, you must try to make them feel that they are being introduced to the life-stories of men and women who really lived, not merely committing a mass of names and dates to memory. French, of course, I shall expect you to talk at mealtimes several days in the week."

"I shall talk French four days of the week and Russian in the remaining three."

"Russian? My dear Miss Hope, no one in the house speaks or understands Russian."

"That will not embarrass me in the least," said Lady Carlotta coldly.

Mrs. Quabarl, to use a colloquial expression, was knocked off her perch. She was one of those imperfectly self-assured individuals who are magnificent and autocratic as long as they are not seriously opposed. The least show of unexpected resistance goes a long way towards rendering them cowed and apologetic. When the new governess failed to express wondering admiration of the large newly-purchased and expensive car, and lightly alluded to the superior advantages of one or two makes which had just been put on the market, the discomfiture of her patroness became almost abject. Her feelings were those which might have animated a general of ancient warfaring days, on beholding his heaviest battle-elephant ignominiously driven off the field by slingers and javelin throwers.

At dinner that evening, although reinforced by her husband, who usually duplicated her opinions and lent her moral support generally, Mrs. Quabarl regained none of her lost ground. The governess not only helped herself well and truly to wine, but held forth with considerable show of critical knowledge on various vintage matters, concerning which the Quabarls were in no wise able to pose as authorities. Previous governesses had limited their conversation on the wine topic to a respectful and doubtless sincere expression of a preference for water. When this one went as far as to recommend a wine firm in whose hands you could not go very far wrong Mrs. Quabarl thought it time to turn the conversation into more usual channels.

"We got very satisfactory references about you from Canon Teep," she observed; "a very estimable man, I should think."

"Drinks like a fish and beats his wife, otherwise a very lovable character," said the governess imperturbably.

"My *dear* Miss Hope! I trust you are exaggerating," exclaimed the Quabarls in unison.

"One must in justice admit that there is some provocation," continued the romancer. "Mrs. Teep is quite the most irritating bridge-player that I have ever sat down with; her leads and declarations would condone a certain amount of brutality in her partner, but to souse her with the contents of the only soda-water syphon in the house on a Sunday afternoon, when one couldn't get another, argues an indifference to the comfort of others which I cannot altogether overlook. You may think me hasty in my judgments, but it was practically on account of the syphon incident that I left."

"We will talk of this some other time," said Mrs. Quabarl hastily.

"I shall never allude to it again," said the governess with decision.

Mr. Quabarl made a welcome diversion by asking what studies the new instructress proposed to inaugurate on the morrow.

"History to begin with," she informed him.

"Ah, history," he observed sagely; "now in teaching them history you must take care to interest them in what they learn. You must make them feel that they are being introduced to the life-stories of men and women who really lived——"

"I've told her all that," interposed Mrs. Quabarl.

"I teach history on the Schartz-Metterklume method," said the governess loftily.

"Ah, yes," said her listeners, thinking it expedient to assume an acquaintance at least with the name.

"What are you children doing out here?" demanded Mrs. Quabarl the next morning, on finding Irene sitting rather glumly at the head of the stairs, while her sister was perched in an attitude of depressed discomfort on the window-seat behind her, with a wolf-skin rug almost covering her.

"We are having a history lesson," came the unexpected reply. "I am supposed to be Rome, and Viola

up there is the she-wolf; not a real wolf, but the figure
of one that the Romans used to set store by—I forget
why. Claude and Wilfrid have gone to fetch the shabby
women."

"The shabby women?"

"Yes, they've got to carry them off. They didn't
want to, but Miss Hope got one of father's fives-bats
and said she'd give them a number nine spanking if they
didn't, so they've gone to do it."

A loud, angry screaming from the direction of the
lawn drew Mrs. Quabarl thither in hot haste, fearful
lest the threatened castigation might even now be in
process of infliction. The outcry, however, came
principally from the two small daughters of the lodge-
keeper, who were being hauled and pushed towards the
house by the panting and dishevelled Claude and Wilfrid, whose task was rendered even more arduous by the
incessant, if not very effectual, attacks of the captured
maidens' small brother. The governess, fives-bat in
hand, sat negligently on the stone balustrade, presiding
over the scene with the cold impartiality of a Goddess
of Battles. A furious and repeated chorus of "I'll tell
muvver" rose from the lodge children, but the lodge-
mother, who was hard of hearing, was for the moment
immersed in the preoccupation of her washtub. After
an apprehensive glance in the direction of the lodge
(the good woman was gifted with the highly militant
temper which is sometimes the privilege of deafness)
Mrs. Quabarl flew indignantly to the rescue of the
struggling captives.

"Wilfrid! Claude! Let those children go at once.

Miss Hope, what on earth is the meaning of this scene?"

"Early Roman history; the Sabine women, don't you know? It's the Schartz-Metterklume method to make children understand history by acting it themselves; fixes it in their memory, you know. Of course, if, thanks to your interference, your boys go through life thinking that the Sabine women ultimately escaped, I really cannot be held responsible."

"You may be very clever and modern, Miss Hope," said Mrs. Quabarl firmly, "but I should like you to leave here by the next train. Your luggage will be sent after you as soon as it arrives."

"I'm not certain exactly where I shall be for the next few days," said the dismissed instructress of youth; "you might keep my luggage till I wire my address. There are only a couple of trunks and some golf-clubs and a leopard cub."

"A leopard cub!" gasped Mrs. Quabarl. Even in her departure this extraordinary person seemed destined to leave a trail of embarrassment behind her.

"Well, it's rather left off being a cub; it's more than half-grown, you know. A fowl every day and a rabbit on Sundays is what it usually gets. Raw beef makes it too excitable. Don't trouble about getting the car for me, I'm rather inclined for a walk."

And Lady Carlotta strode out of the Quabarl horizon.

The advent of the genuine Miss Hope, who had made a mistake as to the day on which she was due to arrive, caused a turmoil which that good lady was quite unused to inspiring. Obviously the Quabarl family had been woefully befooled, but a certain amount of relief came with the knowledge.

"How tiresome for you, dear Carlotta," said her hostess, when the overdue guest ultimately arrived; "how very tiresome losing your train and having to stop overnight in a strange place."

"Oh dear, no," said Lady Carlotta; "not at all tiresome—for me."

## OUR HEARTS WERE YOUNG AND GAY (Chapter IV)
## by Cornelia Otis Skinner and Emily Kimbrough

THE next evening, two days before we were to land, was the night of the ship's concert. I had been asked to participate and had agreed with alacrity. Those were the happy days when with that confidence of a Bernhardt which is vouchsafed only to the amateur I would recite at the drop of a hat and if nobody dropped a hat I'd recite anyway. My repertoire included Noyes's "Highwayman," a few gems in Italian and Negro dialect and (I shudder to recall) Lady Macbeth's sleepwalking scene. I spent an afternoon going over some of my choicer selections in the seclusion of our cabin, and partly because I thought it was professional, but more in order to annoy Emily, went about muttering "Mi-mi-mi" and other embarrassing vocalizations. The morning of the concert dawned, and I woke to the realization that my enthusiasm had lost some of its brightness. My throat was scrapy, my nose stopped up and it was all too apparent that I was giving birth to a fine young cold. I blamed it on the fog of the past three days and tried curing myself by lying in the sun on the top deck, where a series of vicious drafts played on my

most vulnerable parts, and the smokestacks showered
upon me a gentle rain of soot. By mid-afternoon my
throat felt like something dangling from a hook in a
butcher's shop. Someone advised me to gargle salt and
water, and Emily, who went on the theory that if one
pill is good for you, five are even better, mixed up a
concoction so thick with salt it strangled me into near
unconsciousness. Somebody gave me some aspirin and
somebody else gave me pyramidon and somebody else
gave me something else and I swallowed it all quite
indiscriminately, muttering brave remarks to the effect
that "The show must go on." Toward evening I began
to feel better, if slightly light-headed. I gulped down
a cup of soup, dressed and put on a semblance of a
make-up. That was one of the features of my dramatic
display in those days. Whenever I recited, even if in a
small living-room, I went on the theory that a full
theatrical make-up was requisite. On this occasion I
noticed that my eyes were somewhat glazed and that
my cheeks didn't need much rouge, but I attributed
this to excitement. The hour for the concert was announced by a boy banging a gong, and I went to the
main saloon. My act wasn't due till toward the end of
the program, and for the first half I sat at one side
behind the temporary stage. It was one of those routine
ship's concerts. There was the usual little man who told
endless stories in Lancashire dialect beginning with
"I'm minded of the man who . . ." which nobody understood, but over which everybody roared politely; and
that lady with the soprano voice and bust who sang all
about "When I was a young lad before my beard was

gray," to whom everyone listened with fitting expressions of gloom. The orchestra played those selections from Victor Herbert they'd been giving every night, and a sailor with a talent for the trombone obliged with an ear-splitting rendition of "Rocked in the Cradle of the Deep." I listened in a daze, alternately burning with heat and shivering with chill. There was a high sea outside and the boat was doing a lot of pitching and tossing, which made things slightly awkward, as the temporary platform, which was on sort of casters, would roll with the motion until it was stopped on either end by a pillar, in an abrupt contact which would hurtle it back the other way. The performers had to take a wide stance and hold onto any handy bit of furniture for support. My turn was drawing near, and Emily and I both began growing pretty nervous. Just before I went on, that conscientious drinker from Princeton brought me a hooker of straight brandy and that did the trick. It also made me sway, but in rhythm that was in counterpose to that of the ship, so I remained fairly steady. I have absolutely no memory of what I did, but it was apparently a hit. In fact mine was a "success" that could really be called *fou*. This must have been due to the fact that the preceding acts had been so terrible mine must have looked pretty good in contrast. Also the brandy and that mixture of medicine had freed me of all inhibitions and I acted with a fine abandon. There was considerable applause and I was in a flush of what I mistook for success. The concert was followed by a gala dance with confetti and favors and those paper hats middle-aged people, if they're drunk, think are funny. The dance floor was crowded and we were never off it. I knew by now that I was ill but I didn't care. Mine was the "tomorrow we die" spirit. I felt like the Dame aux Camellias and as if a breath would blow me away. With my hectic flush I didn't look much like the Dame aux Camellias and the only breath blowing was my brandy-laden own. I danced madly with everybody. It is like a kaleidoscopic delirium to me now but I can dimly remember the orchestra playing the "Blue Danube" and my whirling in a dizzy waltz with Joe Aub and thinking I was pretty *Alt Wien*. I also have a distinct recollection of going out on deck with that Pride of Princeton and letting him kiss me. Girls didn't kiss much in those days. Those who did were considered "fast." We still had ringing in our consciences the maternal admonition that "boys would lose all respect for us if we did." Whenever I fell from grace in this fashion (which was whenever I had the slightest opportunity) I'd go through an aftermath of abject penitence, accusing myself of being a Magdalen . . . without having a very clear idea of what a Magdalen was, then when the occasion next offered itself I'd do it all over again. That night my abandon was so complete I felt no remorse. As a matter of fact I was incapable of feeling anything beyond a sore throat and a perpetual dry heat-wave.

I have no memory of ever getting to bed but I certainly remember waking up in the early morning and thinking I had a combination of pneumonia and diphtheria with a slight sprinkling of small-pox. I was much too ill to move. My breathing came with effort and a sound like a threshing machine. I moaned and lay staring at the ceiling waiting for the Fatal Reaper. Emily woke and looked at me and it was clear she was scared. She dressed and went forth to summon the ship's physician, then prompted by some fortuitous inner hunch, decided it might be wiser to get hold of one of our doctor friends. She found Joe Aub and in a frenzy yanked him down to the cabin. He looked me over, listened to my lungs and punched my stomach which, with the memory of our recent "Blue Danube" whirl bright within me, at once embarrassed and rather pleased me. Then he told me to say "Ah" and after I had he looked extremely grave.

"Have you ever had measles?" he asked.

"Measles? Why, no."

"Well, my dear girl," he said, "you're coming down with a hell of a case."

"Measles!" I couldn't believe him. "But I thought I was past the age for such things."

"Adults can have measles," he said. "And when they do it's pretty serious."

"But how on earth . . ." Then I remembered Les Eboulements. Those picturesque little French Canadian interiors, the windows and doors hermetically closed, and the little children running about underfoot, some with a rash, others flushed, and all of them coughing generously in very direction.

Paul White came down and verified Joe's diagnosis, and then came the problem of what to do. Nobody must know about it. The boat was due at Cherbourg early next morning and a few hours later Emily and I were to disembark at Southampton. If it became known I had measles they'd never let me land. The ship, after a day or two in Southampton, was to go on to Hamburg and I'd be sent in all probability to a German quarantine hospital. The prospect was too awful. I lay back on the pillows and amid a torrent of tears wailed that I didn't want to go to Germany and be nursed by a walkyrie. They pacified me as best they could. Paul and Joe promised to give me all medical attention, even if of a clandestine nature, and Emily could nurse me. She had had measles (and that was one more thing that made me feel inferior, like her spouting Greek or her annoying ability to quote William James). I'd be all right for twenty-four hours, as the rash wouldn't come out for a time, and somehow they'd manage to devise some way to smuggle me into England. (One might have thought I was a pearl necklace or a shipment of narcotics.)

The three of them went up on deck and into a huddle behind a lifeboat, where they made a solemn agreement. Emily would not report my contagious condition to the ship's doctor and neither would Paul or Joe. They might be disbarred or unfrocked or whatever it is that happens to medical men, but they'd throw in their lot with ours and take the risk. My parents were planning to be at Southampton. We'd had a wire saying so. Once having safely run the gamut of the health inspector I could go direct to a hotel where Mother would take care of me. Joe had to get off at Cherbourg but Paul would go on through to England with us and see me started on my way to recovery.

Mother would in due course write the captain that what we'd thought was a cold had turned into measles, so they could fumigate the cabin and prevent any further spread of the disease,—as if, the preceding evening, I hadn't already spread it in a manner capable of starting an all-high European epidemic. The main hope was that my rash wouldn't manifest itself until they'd gotten me safely on land. They returned to tell me all this, but I was too sick to care. The two doctors managed to get just enough of the proper medicine from the ship's infirmary without exciting too much suspicion, and I spent the forenoon in a stupor, roused now and then by Emily, who would shine a painfully bright miniature flash-light (I believe they were called "bug-lights") in my face, study its condition and say in the tone of someone trying to pep up a losing team: "You hold that rash back!"

Later I was left comparatively alone. The day was balmy, there was a smell of land in the air and after those hours of dank fog and slate-colored sky Emily was much too elated to bother about my measles. The misty outline of a headland lay like a cloud bank on the northern horizon. Gulls flew out to form a circling, soaring convoy, their cries like the creak of a pulley, the late afternoon sun gilding their fat snowy bellies. Fishing boats suddenly appeared and small craft began dotting the sea, making it seem a friendly lake. Occasionally someone would call out from the calm water below in a voice that rang with the unmistakable lilt of Ireland. Night came on, and over the port bow the great warning of the Fastness light began flashing.

Emily watched it all with wonder and a few tears, and then came down to our little pest-hole to see if I were still alive and to do some packing. She moved me into the upper berth because she said it was airier and I'd be more comfortable up there, but I suspect her real motive was to get me out of the way. Then she proceeded to pack in the manner of an excited nineteen-year-old girl, which is the same manner as that of someone salvaging odds and ends from a burning house. We'd struck a ground swell and the ship was rolling slowly but decidedly. Things Emily was in the act of packing slid alternately under the berth and the couch. Bottles fell over and tooth brushes clattered about in the basin. Emily cursed and I groaned. Every now and then she'd make me down a pill or a spoonful of medicine. At other times she'd hand me a glass of something to gargle, then holding up a homely object known in some locales as a "thunder-mug" she'd say in the dulcet tone of a night nurse, "Come on, dear, spit for Emily." It was a ghastly night. I was really awfully sick and Emily was really awfully scared. I tossed and moaned and Emily in helpless despair kept getting up and putting cool cloths on my brow and making me spit for Emily. Neither of us slept until toward dawn when from sheer exhaustion we dozed off and immediately afterward our slumber was shattered by those early morning noises which all steamship personnel consider a necessary accompaniment to coming into harbor. Baggage is hurtled and banged along passageways, people scamper quite a lot, and a sleepy cabin-boy whangs a gong for some special reveille-hour breakfast which nobody dreams of going to.

We were coming into Cherbourg and Emily went up on deck to look at it and to indulge in another spell of emotional appreciation. One's view of France after a long absence, no matter how well one knows it, is something to bring a slight lump into the throat. But to the girl of nineteen, seeing it for the first time, it was a thing to produce a lump the size of a healthy orange. A hazy poilu-blue sky, flecked with those harmless little clouds that seem to form only over France; a smooth grey sea, gashed by a long breakwater the color of a dark wet seal. Along the breakwater a handful of men in faded blue pants, red handkerchiefs tied loosely about their throats, sat fishing the way Frenchmen from time immemorial have fished, which is with a long pole, the air of a *philosophe* and no thought of ever catching a fish. In the misty distance lay the sweet French coast, the ancient town, like a model for a stage set, and the jetty with its custom-house striped like peppermint candy to indicate you were approaching a country where people were gay and, just in case you weren't certain it was France, on a nearby building, a huge painted likeness of that dreadful leering baby, the Savon Cadum ad.

The ship had dropped anchor and a small French tender had pulled up alongside and taken off such passengers as were destined for Cherbourg. They were about to push off, and there was that usual *crise de nerfs* which seems to accompany all French maritime manoeuvres. Whistles blew shrilly, sailors with red pompons either rushed about gesticulating madly or stood quite still with elaborate indifference and shrugged while people in the pilot house engaged themselves in vituperative argument, and frazzled Americans ambled hopelessly about looking for bits of missing luggage. Seething with activity, the tender started for shore, and the *Empress,* with a short snort of relief from her horn, began hauling in her anchor. A few yards away there burst from the tender a series of whistle tootings and bell ringings mingled with that wonderful Gallic cry *Attention! Attention* which is applicable to all emergencies from that of a child about to spill the milk to the Eiffel Tower about to fall. The little vessel backed water furiously, came about at an angle like a contestant for the America's Cup, and chugged up alongside again. Lines were thrown across and everybody yelled at the top of their lungs. Emily's French then was Bryn Mawr entrance requirement, and she didn't understand what was being said exactly, but she swears that a few seconds later someone on our lower deck leaned perilously out across the intervening space and solemnly handed something to a pompous little French immigration official. Then everybody laughed and one or two screamed *Merci infiniment!* and the tender pulled away and steamed jauntily for shore. The object of the commotion was a bottle of ink which the immigration official had had the unbelievable carelessness to leave behind. He'd got it back now and everybody was happy. Emily put her head down on the rail and cried again because the French were turning out just as she thought they would.

She returned to our cabin and she says that Lord, I did

look awful! My face was swollen into the shape of the harvest moon. It was the color of Chinese lacquer and it glistened. Those spots were gathering but as yet hadn't burgeoned, which was one reason I felt so wretchedly. Emily told me to keep on holding them back, paralyzing me with the threat that if I didn't the quarantine ward in Hamburg was yearning for me. I lay there in misery trying to control my rash and going over in my throbbing brain what I could summon up of German declensions. I tried to tell her where my things were but talking was too difficult and I went off into momentary spells of feverish oblivion. Through it all I was dimly aware of a little boy who kept sticking his head in at our door and saying:

"Would you care to see the boots, Madam?"

"Boots?" Emily would answer, "No."

In a few minutes he'd be back again with the same question to which Emily would snap back the same response, each time growing more irritated. The prospect of getting me off the ship had put her nerves on edge and at his fifth or sixth appearance she lost her temper.

"*No*," she roared at the hapless child, "I don't want to see any boots! I don't ride and I don't fish and what I'd want boots for I can't imagine. And whatever shoe company has brought on board a collection has chosen a very peculiar time for it if you ask me."

I then realized what it was all about and sick as I was laughed till I cried.

"He's the 'Boots,' you zany!" I managed to say.

"He's polished our shoes every day and the poor little devil wants a tip."

Emily said "Oh" somewhat crossly and gave it to him.

My one compensation in being ill was that Emily would have to shoulder the trying responsibility of tipping. I have never mastered the knowledge of the proper scale of tipping on a liner and I resent the whole idea. English stewards and stewardesses have a way of looking like earls and duchesses incognito and the thought of giving them a tip, call it a "gratuity" even, embarrasses me to such a point, I usually slip whatever I'm giving into a sealed envelope, hand it to them as if it were a valentine and run. If they are not the earl and duchess type, they're that mercurial variety who are all smiles when you get on board and sour-pusses when you land. Whatever you give them they won't like. If it's too little they look as if you'd robbed their child's bank and if it's too much they regard you with contempt, and if it's the proper amount they look dissatisfied on principle.

Luckily ours were the less aristocratic species of employee. The stewardess, a large motherly soul, helped dress me and the steward said to leave everything to him. We didn't know what that meant exactly but it sounded reassuring. One thing we were leaving him, at any rate, was a generous quantity of measle germs.

Joe Aub had left us at Cherbourg. Paul White and Emily, the only ones who knew my guilty secret, had to fix me up so I could pass the health inspector. From the sight of me this looked to be a task equivalent to

fixing up a Rogers Group to pass for a Michelangelo.
It was even doubtful if I'd get by with my passport
picture. I struggled into my clothes, and with what
negligible strength I had, tried camouflaging my face
with slathers of foundation cream and half the contents
of a box of face powder. The effect was that of someone who had been ducking for apples in a paper-
hanger's bucket. This thick coating worked for a time
but then the intense heat of my face baked it into a sort
of dry *papier-maché* which, if I moved any facial
muscle, cracked and revealed glimpses of that gleaming
flesh. My parched lips I made up with one of those
orange lipsticks which is supposed to change color once
it's applied. It did, all right. Only instead of a delicate
shade of coral, the medicine I'd been taking or something turned it into a lurid violet. With some curious
notion that it would distract from the rest of my visage,
I painted my mouth to look twice its normal size (and
it's no sweetheart rosebud to begin with). Emily asked
me gently if I wasn't being a bit spectacular and I said
not at all, it was merely a case of understanding the art
of the theatre, and that silenced her. The hat I selected
to wear was a bright red number with a cock feather
that swung down rakishly under my chin. I used to
think it made me look rather like Irene Bordoni. But
I didn't look like Irene Bordoni then. Fortunately for
the dignity of the human race, I didn't look like anything that had ever before existed. If during the crossing, Emily and I, owing to our failure to whip up any
feminine attachments, had earned the reputation of
being scarlet women, I was certainly fixed up fine for

the part. Emily and Paul, with saint-like tolerance, refrained from comment, nor did they say anything when I topped off my startling appearance with a flowing white veil which, I pointed out, would make me less conspicuous. I guess I'd gotten a little delirious by then.

We were nearing Southampton and a second wireless arrived from Mother and Father saying they'd be at the dock and couldn't wait to see us. Catching a glimpse of myself in the mirror, I wondered how they'd feel about waiting after they did.

Emily and Paul managed somehow or other to get me upstairs and into line for health inspection. They stood me between them so that in case I collapsed they'd be there to break my fall. I flashed a ghastly smile like a ballet-dancer's at the inspector, who merely shuddered and passed me as rapidly as possible. The passport gent never even looked up. The only persons who paid any attention to me were the other passengers who stared in bewilderment at the white veil and that art of the theatre make-up which gleamed through it. The ship by now was coming up to the dock and in half an hour we'd be ashore. I was propped against some cushions in a very dark corner of a deserted card room and told not to move, which, in view of the fact I scarcely could, seemed a superfluous admonition. For what seemed to me hours I sat there swathed in my white veil and utter wretchedness. Nobody came near me except a little girl who all at once skipped into the room, spied me and came to a dead stop. For some uneasy seconds she stood before me gazing with wonder. Then in an awed whisper she said, "Do you tell fortunes?" and without waiting for an answer turned tail and ran.

Emily had gone out on deck to locate my parents. She didn't have much trouble. They were easily distinguishable, the darlings, there in the thick of the crowd staring up at the ship,—Father as if he'd been interrupted in the midst of reading and only half of him had come, and Mother like an excited little bird looking for us all over the vessel. She kept waving furiously at passengers who bore not the remotest resemblance to us, immigrants in the steerage, cooks in the galley, officers on the deck and she even blew a kiss or two at a lifeboat. Eventually she located Emily and pointed her out to Father, who had seen her for some time and had been waving intermittently in a vague but happy manner. Mother, cupping her mouth and standing on tiptoe as if that would make her voice carry higher, called out:

"Darling! Darling!" Then she added, "We've a surprise for you girls!"

"We've got a surprise for you too," Emily shouted back, and Mother again nodded with the tolerant smile one bestows on a child who comes up with a present of a mud pie. Then she and Father in unison sang out, "Where's Cornelia?"

This was the question Emily had been dreading, and having no answer for it she merely smiled and waved and pretended she hadn't heard. They halloed the question again and again but her only response was to wave and smile inanely. My parents gradually became aware that all was not as it should be. They recalled the experience of receiving that cryptic mid-ocean message saying that everything was all right and it had turned out to be a minor shipwreck. After the third demand, and Emily's third evasion, Father felt such nonsense had gone far enough and in a tone that made even the men on the bridge turn around, bellowed "WHERE IS CORNELIA???"

"Oh," Emily called back as lightly as she could and still be heard, "she's inside. She's got a little cold."

Mother turned pale and clutched Father's arm. "It's her appendix, Otis! I always knew her appendix would catch up with her!"

Father said nonsense, he didn't think it was my appendix at all but from his expression it was obvious he thought it might be anything from laryngitis to leprosy.

The gangplank was lowered, and down it Emily rocketed like a ball in a bowling alley, rushed straight up to Mother and Father, embraced them and said in the tense sotto-voce of a conspirator, "Don't say a word to anybody. Don't even whisper it because if it becomes known we are lost. But Cornelia has measles."

Whereat Father, in that voice which for fifty years thrilled the topmost occupant of the highest seat in the gallery, whooped "MEASLES!!!" and would have whooped it again only Mother, who had sized up the situation, deftly and discreetly put a hand with a handkerchief in it over his mouth.

"Where is she, Emily?" she asked quietly.

Emily told them they had me cooling in a dark corner, and that the doctor was with me. Telling Father to follow, Mother started up the gangplank. An officer told her she wasn't allowed on board and some able-bodied seamen held out restraining arms. What happened to them was what happened to anyone on whom Mother shed her charm. She just smiled at them, and in her beautiful voice murmured a lot of charming jargon that made no sense whatsoever . . . about her child and a friend . . . at Bryn Mawr together . . . just outside Philadelphia . . . they had lived there too but not recently . . . and they were all going in a motor somewhere, but that was a surprise for the dear children . . . so brave, too, although she hadn't approved of their being alone in the first place . . . but of course Miss Mary was a tower of strength. And somehow she got up the gangplank and onto the boat. People just gave way, a trifle dazed.

She was pretty dazed herself when she saw me and so I guess was Father for I still have a distinct picture of him staring at me with the same expression with which, as Macbeth, he must have stared at Banquo's ghost. Then, I remember, he collapsed onto a silly gilt chair and laughed till the tears ran down his cheeks. This hurt my feelings acutely and Mother was indignant with him and couldn't understand his callous glee. But he kept saying, "It's the make-up, Maud!" and he'd go off again into a fresh paroxysm. Perhaps it was just as well that he did, for Mother at sight of me had taken me in her arms and put my fantastic head on her soft little bosom, and in that gentle and familiar sanctuary I forgot about being Irene Bordoni or Theda Bara and would doubtless have sobbed my heart out if Father's wild hilarity hadn't cramped the style of my self-pity.

They led me onto the deck, where in the harsh light of day I looked a good deal worse. Bits of that facial calcimine had flaked off revealing the fact that those long-awaited spots were coming out. But somehow the four of them got me off the ship and onto the dock. Even on terra firma we weren't out of danger of discovery. I might still be nabbed and sent to an isolation ward of sorts. The plan was to go to the leading hostelry of Southampton acting as if nothing were amiss. Father and Emily would do the registering while Mother and Paul would follow with me, whisking me as swiftly as possible through the lobby and up to a quiet room without letting on to the innocent innkeeper and his guileless employees the horrid fact that they were harboring a not-so-distant relative of Typhoid Mary.

I put on really quite a commendable act; laughed and chatted giddily, passed the customs in a dazed but grand manner, and sprang with a spurt of super-human activity into a touring car the family had waiting there for us all. This was the surprise Mother had in store for us. She and Father had struck a bargain with the driver of an open Daimler, and in it we were to journey to London in leisurely fashion, stopping off at places of interest on the way. Heigh-ho! It was a pretty notion! We now journeyed from the dock to the hotel.

The hotel was one of those British terminal ones, part caravansary, part ticket office, right on the tracks, the sort that gives the impression of having engines running in and out of the potted palms. In the lobby I kept up my act of laughter and carefree abandon. We were allotted rooms, although the clerk gaped at me in my white veil and formidable complexion. But I carried it off, and didn't let down until I reached the room. There, once they got me in bed, I went completely and noisily delirious. And my but that was fun! With the porter and the chambermaid coming in and God knows who else, and me sitting up in bed with the art of the theatre sagging on my face but still lurid. My four attendants would close in around me as if I were giving them football signals, screening me as best they could, then trying to hold me down as soon as the coast was clear. At last the outsiders departed and with them the threat of being found out. I felt like a French aristocrat who had escaped the talons of the revolution, although the only one I remotely resembled was the Scarlet Pimpernell. I sank back on a burning pillow, and for the next few days I was awfully, awfully sick.

## CRISP NEW BILLS FOR MR. TEAGLE by Frank Sullivan

COMING down in the elevator, Clement Teagle noticed an unwonted cordiality in Steve, the elevator boy, and Harry, the doorman, but thought nothing of it until he stopped at the bank on the corner to cash a check and noticed the date.

December the twenty-fourth.

Good gosh, Mr. Teagle thought, I haven't bought a present for Essie yet.

Then he remembered Steve and Harry.

His eye caught a legend on a Christmas placard on the wall. "It is more blessed to give than to receive," said the placard.

"Oh, yeah?" remarked Mr. Teagle, who, alas, was somewhat of a cynic.

Grumbling, he tore up the check he had started to write, and made out another, for a larger amount.

"Will you please give me new bills?" he asked.

"Indeed I shall," said Mr. Freyer, the teller, cordially.

He counted out one hundred dollars in new bills—*crisp* new bills—and passed them over to Mr. Teagle.

Then he tore up the check and handed the fragments to Mr. Teagle.

"Don't be alarmed, Mr. Teagle," said Mr. Freyer. "The Bank of the Manhattan Company wants you to accept that hundred dollars as a slight token of its esteem, with its best wishes for a Merry Christmas. You have been a loyal depositor here these many years. You have overdrawn fewer times than most of your fellow-depositors. You never argue about your monthly statements. You never feel insulted when a new teller identifies your signature before cashing your checks. You are the kind of depositor who makes banking a joy, and I want to take this opportunity to tell you that we fellows around here, although we are not very demonstrative about that sort of thing, love you very much. A Merry Christmas to you."

"You mean the bank is *giving* me this money?" said Mr. Teagle.

"That is the impression I was trying to convey," said Mr. Freyer, with a chuckle.

"Why—uh, thanks, Mr. Freyer. And—and thank the bank. This is—um—quite a surprise."

"Say no more about it, Mr. Teagle. And every Christmas joy to you, sir."

When Mr. Teagle left the bank he was somewhat perturbed, and a little stunned. He went back to the apartment to place the crisp new bills in envelopes for the boys, and as he left the elevator at his floor, Steve handed him an envelope.

"Merry Christmas, Mr. Teagle," said Steve.

"Thanks, Steve," said Mr. Teagle. "I'll—I'll be wishing you one a little later," he added significantly.

"You don't need to, Mr. Teagle," said Steve. "A man like you wishes the whole world Merry Christmas every day, just by living."

"Oh, Steve, damn nice of you to say that, but I'm sure it's not deserved," said Mr. Teagle, modesty struggling with a feeling that Steve spoke no more than the simple truth.

"Well, I guess we won't argue about *that*," said Steve, gazing affectionately at Mr. Teagle.

I really believe that lad meant it, thought Mr. Teagle, as he let himself into the apartment. I really believe he did.

Mr. Teagle opened the envelope Steve had handed him. A crisp new five-dollar bill fell out.

Downstairs, in the lobby, a few minutes later, Steve was protesting.

"I tell you it wasn't a mistake, Mr. Teagle. I put the bill in there on purpose. For you."

"Steve, I couldn't take—"

"But you *can* take it, and you *will*, Mr. Teagle. And a very Merry Christmas to you."

"Then you accept this Steve, and a Merry Christmas to *you*."

"Oh, no, Mr. Teagle. Not this year. You have been pretty swell to we fellows all the years you've lived here. Now it's our turn."

"You bet it is," said Harry, the doorman, joining them and pressing a crisp new ten-dollar bill into Mr. Teagle's hand. "Merry Christmas, Mr. Teagle. Buy yourself something foolish with this. I only wish it could be more, but I've had a rather bad year in the market."

"I think the boys on the night shift have a little surprise for Mr. Teagle, too," said Steve, with a twinkle in his eye.

Just then the superintendent came up.

"Well, well, well," he said jovially. "Who have we got here? Mr. Teagle, it may interest you to hear that I've been having a little chat about you with a certain old gentleman with a long, snowy beard and twinkling little eyes. Know who I mean?"

"Santa Claus?" Mr. Teagle asked.

"None other. And guess what! He asked me if you had been a good boy this year, and I was delighted to be able to tell him you had been, that you hadn't complained about the heat, hadn't run your radio after eleven at night, and hadn't had any late parties. Well, sir, you should have seen old Santa's face. He was tickled to hear it. Said he always knew you were a good boy. And what do you suppose he did?"

"What?" asked Mr. Teagle.

"He asked me to give you this and to tell you to buy yourself something for Christmas with it. Something foolish."

The super pressed a crisp new twenty-dollar bill upon Mr. Teagle.

"Merry Christmas, Mr. Teagle," said the super.

"Merry Christmas, Mr. Teagle," said Steve, the elevator boy.

"Merry Christmas, Mr. Teagle," said Harry, the doorman.

"Merry Christmas," said Mr. Teagle, in a voice you could scarcely hear. Remembering that he had to buy a present for Essie, he walked out, with the air of a bewildered gazelle. He was in a very, very puzzled state of mind as he walked down East Fifty-first Street, an agitation which did not subside when the proprietor of a cigarstore on Third Avenue rushed out, pressed a box of cigars on him, cried, "Merry Christmas, stranger!," and rushed back into his shop without another word.

To rush out of your store and give a box of cigars to a perfect stranger! And those boys at the apartment house! *And* the super!

Mr. Teagle thought of the many times he had grumbled at being kept waiting a few minutes for the elevator or for a taxi. He felt ashamed. By George, Mr. Teagle thought, maybe Dickens was right.

Mr. Teagle approached the business of choosing a present for his wife in a far less carping spirit than was his Christmas wont.

I'll get Essie something that'll knock her eye out, he thought. She's a good old girl and she deserves a lot of credit for living with a grouch like me all these years. The best is none too good for her.

Suiting the action to the word, Mr. Teagle turned in at Cartier's and asked to see some square-cut emeralds. He selected one that could have done duty on a traffic light.

"I'm afraid I haven't the cash on me," he told the

clerk. "I'll give you a check, and you can call the bank and verify—"

"That will not be necessary, sir," said the clerk, with a radiant smile. "You are Mr. Clement Teagle, I believe. In that case, Cartier wishes you to accept this trinket with the Christmas greetings of the firm. We are only sorry that you did not see fit to choose a diamond stomacher. Cartier will feel honored that one of its emeralds is adorning the finger of the wife of a man like Clement Teagle, a man four-square, a man who is a credit—All right, all right, all *right*, Mr. Teagle! Not another word, please. Cartier is adamant. You take this emerald or we may grow ugly about it. And don't lose it, sir, or I venture to say your good wife will give you Hail Columbia. Good day, sir, and God rest ye."

Mr. Teagle found himself on the street. He accosted the first passerby.

"Excuse me, stranger, but would you mind pinching me?"

"Certainly not, certainly not," said the stranger, cheerily. "There. Feel better?"

"Yes. Thank you very much," said Mr. Teagle.

"Here, buy yourself something for Christmas," said the stranger, pressing Mr. Teagle's hand. Mr. Teagle looked in the hand and found himself the possessor of a crisp new fifty-dollar bill.

At Fifth Avenue and Fifty-seventh Street, a Park & Tilford attendant rushed out and draped a huge basket, bedecked with ribbons and holly, on Mr. Teagle's arm.

"Everything drinkable for the Yuletide dinner, with

love and kisses from Park & Tilford," whispered the clerk, jovially. "Tell your wife to be sure and put the champagne in ice early, so it will be nice and cold."

"Oh, come on, come on," protested the butcher at Madison Avenue and Sixty-first Street. "Don't tell me you're too loaded down to carry a simple little turkey home, with the affectionate Christmas wishes of Shaffer's Market."

Mr. Shaffer laughed the rich laugh of the contented butcher.

"Don't take me too seriously when I say 'simple little turkey,'" he said. "That bird you got would make Roosevelt's Christmas turkey look like a hummingbird. An undernourished hummingbird. Pay for it? Certainly you won't pay for it! What do you take me for? It's Christmas. And you are Clement Teagle."

"Am I?" said Mr. Teagle, humbly.

Long before he reached home, Mr. Teagle had had such a plethora of gifts pressed upon him by friendly strangers that there was nothing to do but load them into a taxicab. And Mr. Teagle was not quite as surprised as he might have been earlier in the day when the driver refused to accept any money, but grinned and said, "Let's just charge this trip to good old St. Nick."

"Why, Clem!" said Mrs. Teagle, when, with the aid of the entire house staff, Mr. Teagle had deposited his gifts in the dining-room. "Why, Clem, I already *bought* a turkey! Clem, you've been drinking."

"I have *not!*" Mr. Teagle shouted.

"Well, don't get on your high horse," said Mrs.

Teagle. "It's Christmas Eve. I don't mind. Only—you know your stomach. And you do look funny."

"I may look funny, but I have not been drinking," Mr. Teagle insisted. "Look! H-h-h-h-h-h."

His breath was as the new-mown hay.

"See what I got you for Christmas, Essie." Mrs. Teagle opened the jewel case and the emerald gleamed up at her. It was a moment before she could speak.

"No, Clem," she said. "You work too hard for your money. I don't deserve this. I won't take it from you. You've been too good to me as it is. I don't want any Christmas present from you, dear. I want to *give* you one—and oh, by the way, Clem, before I forget it, the funniest thing happened this afternoon. The income-tax man was here, the federal income-tax man. Said he just dropped in to wish you a Merry Christmas. He left this check for your entire last year's income tax. He said the government wants to give it back to you as a token of affection and in recognition of your many superb qualities as a citizen and—oh, I can't remember everything he said, but he made quite a flowery speech about you, dear—Why, Clem, what's the matter?"

Mr. Teagle had burst into tears.

"A Merry Christmas, Essie," he said, through his sobs, "and, in the language of Tiny Tim, God Bless Us Every One."

## MISS RENNSDALE ACCEPTS by Booth Tarkington

ONE-TWO-THREE; one-two-three—glide!" said Professor Bartet, emphasizing his instructions by a brisk collision of his palms at "glide." "One-two-three; one-two-three—glide!"

The school week was over, at last, but Penrod's troubles were not.

Round and round the ballroom went the seventeen struggling little couples of the Friday Afternoon Dancing Class. Round and round went their reflections with them, swimming rhythmically in the polished, dark floor—white and blue and pink for the girls; black, with dabs of white, for the white-collared, white-gloved boys; and sparks and slivers of high light everywhere as the glistening pumps flickered along the surface like a school of flying fish. Every small pink face—with one exception—was painstaking and set for duty. It was a conscientious little merry-go-round.

"One-two-three; one-two-three—glide! One-two-three; one-two-three—glide! One-two-th——Ha! Mister Penrod Schofield, you lose the step. Your left foot! No, no! This is the left! See—like me! Now again! One-two-three; one-two-three—glide! Better! Much

better! Again! One-two-three; one-two-three—gl—
Stop! Mr. Penrod Schofield, this dancing class is pro-
vided by the kind parents of the pupilses as much to
learn the mannerss of good societies as to dance. You
think you shall ever see a gentleman in good societies
to tickle his partner in the dance till she say Ouch?
Never! I assure you it is not done. Again! Now then!
Piano, please! One-two-three; one-two-three—glide!
Mr. Penrod Schofield, your right foot—your right foot!
No, no! Stop!"

The merry-go-round came to a standstill.

"Mr. Penrod Schofield and partner"—Professor
Bartet wiped his brow—"will you kindly observe me?
One-two-three—glide! So! Now then—no; you will
please keep your places, ladies and gentlemen. Mr.
Penrod Schofield, I would puttickly like your attention;
this is for you!"

"Pickin' on me again!" murmured the smouldering
Penrod to his small, unsympathetic partner. "Can't let
me alone a minute!"

"Mister Georgie Bassett, please step to the centre,"
said the professor.

Mr. Bassett complied with modest alacrity.

"Teacher's pet!" whispered Penrod hoarsely. He had
nothing but contempt for Georgie Bassett. The parents,
guardians, aunts, uncles, cousins, governesses, house-
maids, cooks, chauffeurs and coachmen, appertaining to
the members of the dancing class, all dwelt in the same
part of town and shared certain communal theories; and
among the most firmly established was that which
maintained Georgie Bassett to be the Best Boy in Town.

Contrariwise, the unfortunate Penrod, largely because of his recent dazzling but disastrous attempts to control forces far beyond him, had been given a clear title as the Worst Boy in Town. (Population, 135,000.) To precisely what degree his reputation was the product of his own energies cannot be calculated. It was Marjorie Jones who first applied the description, in its definite simplicity, the day after the "pageant," and, possibly, her frequent and effusive repetitions of it, even upon wholly irrelevant occasions, had something to do with its prompt and quite perfect acceptance by the community.

"Miss Rennsdale will please do me the fafer to be Mr. Georgie Bassett's partner for one moment," said Professor Bartet. "Mr. Penrod Schofield will please give his attention. Miss Rennsdale and Mister Bassett, obliche me, if you please. Others please watch. Piano, please! Now then!"

Miss Rennsdale, aged eight—the youngest lady in the class—and Mr. Georgie Bassett one-two-three-glided with consummate technique for the better education of Penrod Schofield. It is possible that amber-curled, beautiful Marjorie felt that she, rather than Miss Rennsdale, might have been selected as the example of perfection—or perhaps her remark was only woman.

"Stopping everybody for that boy!" said Marjorie.

Penrod, across the circle from her, heard distinctly —nay, he was obviously intended to hear; but over a scorched heart he preserved a stoic front. Whereupon Marjorie whispered derisively in the ear of her partner, Maurice Levy, who wore a pearl pin in his tie.

"Again, please, everybody—ladies and gentlemen!" cried Professor Bartet. "Mister Penrod Schofield, if you please, pay puttickly attention! Piano, please! Now then!"

The lesson proceeded. At the close of the hour Professor Bartet stepped to the centre of the room and clapped his hands for attention.

"Ladies and gentlemen, if you please to seat yourselves quietly," he said; "I speak to you now about to-morrow. As you all know—— Mister Penrod Schofield, I am not sticking up in a tree outside that window! If you do me the fafer to examine I am here, insides of the room. Now then! Piano, pl—no, I do not wish the piano! As you all know, this is the last lesson of the season until next October. To-morrow is our special afternoon; beginning three o'clock, we dance the cotillon. But this afternoon comes the test of mannerss. You must see if each know how to make a little formal call like a grown-up people in good societies. You have had good, perfect instruction; let us see if we know how to per-form like societies ladies and gentlemen twenty-six years of age.

"Now, when you are dismissed each lady will go to her home and prepare to receive a call. The gentlemen will allow the ladies time to reach their houses and to prepare to receive callers; then each gentleman will call upon a lady and beg the pleasure to engage her for a partner in the cotillon to-morrow. You all know the correct, proper form for these calls, because didn't I work teaching you last lesson till I thought I would drop dead? Yes! Now each gentleman, if he reach a lady's house behind some other gentleman, then he must go somewhere else to a lady's house, and keep calling until he secures a partner; so, as there are the same number of both, everybody shall have a partner.

"Now please all remember that if in case—— Mister Penrod Schofield, when you make your call on a lady I beg you please remember that gentlemen in good societies do not scratch the back in societies as you appear to attempt; so please allow the hands to rest carelessly in the lap. Now please all remember that if in case—— Mister Penrod Schofield, if you please! Gentlemen in societies do not scratch the back by causing frictions between it and the back of your chair, either! Nobody else is itching here! *I* do not itch! I cannot talk if you must itch! In the name of Heaven, why must you always itch? What was I saying? Where —ah! the cotillon—yes! For the cotillon it is important nobody shall fail to be here to-morrow; but if any one should be so very ill he cannot possible come he must write a very polite note of regrets in the form of good societies to his engaged partner to excuse himself—and he must give the reason.

"I do not think anybody is going to be that sick to-morrow—no; and I will find out and report to parents if anybody would try it and not be. But it is important for the cotillon that we have an even number of so many couples, and if it should happen that some one comes and her partner has sent her a polite note that he has genuine reasons why he cannot come, the note must be handed at once to me, so that I arrange some other partner. Is all understood? Yes. The gentlemen will remember now to allow the ladies plenty of time to reach their houses and prepare to receive calls. Ladies and gentlemen, I thank you for your polite attention."

It was nine blocks to the house of Marjorie Jones; but Penrod did it in less than seven minutes from a flying start—such was his haste to lay himself and his hand for the cotillon at the feet of one who had so recently spoken unamiably of him in public. He had not yet learned that the only safe male rebuke to a scornful female is to stay away from her—especially if that is what she desires. However, he did not wish to rebuke her; simply and ardently he wished to dance the cotillon with her. Resentment was swallowed up in hope.

The fact that Miss Jones' feeling for him bore a striking resemblance to that of Simon Legree for Uncle Tom, deterred him not at all. Naturally, he was not wholly unconscious that when he should lay his hand for the cotillon at her feet it would be her inward desire to step on it; but he believed that if he were first in the field Marjorie would have to accept. These things are governed by law.

It was his fond intention to reach her house even in advance of herself, and with grave misgiving he beheld a large automobile at rest before the sainted gate. Forthwith, a sinking feeling became a portent inside him as little Maurice Levy emerged from the front door of the house.

" 'Lo, Penrod!" said Maurice airily.

"What you doin' in there?" inquired Penrod.

"In where?"

"In Marjorie's."

"Well, what shouldn't I be doin' in Marjorie's?" Mr. Levy returned indignantly. "I was inviting her for my partner in the cotillon—what you s'pose?"

"You haven't got any right to!" Penrod protested hotly. "You can't do it yet."

"I did do it yet!" said Maurice.

"You can't!" insisted Penrod. "You got to allow them time first. He said the ladies had to be allowed time to prepare."

"Well, ain't she had time to prepare?"

"When?" Penrod demanded, stepping close to his rival threateningly. "I'd like to know when——"

"When?" echoed the other with shrill triumph. "When? Why, in mamma's sixty-horse powder limousine automobile, what Marjorie came home with me in! I guess that's when!"

An impulse in the direction of violence became visible upon the countenance of Penrod.

"I expect you need some wiping down," he began dangerously. "I'll give you sumpthing to remem——"

"Oh, you will!" Maurice cried with astonishing truculence, contorting himself into what he may have considered a posture of defense. "Let's see you try it, you—you itcher!"

For the moment, defiance from such a source was dumfounding. Then, luckily, Penrod recollected something and glanced at the automobile.

Perceiving therein not only the alert chauffeur but the magnificent outlines of Mrs. Levy, his enemy's mother, he manœuvred his lifted hand so that it seemed he had but meant to scratch his ear.

"Well, I guess I better be goin'," he said casually. "See you t'-morrow!"

Maurice mounted to the lap of luxury, and Penrod strolled away with an assumption of careless ease which was put to a severe strain when, from the rear window of the car, a sudden protuberance in the nature of a small, dark, curly head shrieked scornfully:

"Go on—you big stiff!"

The cotillon loomed dismally before Penrod now; but it was his duty to secure a partner and he set about it with a dreary heart. The delay occasioned by his fruitless attempt on Marjorie and the altercation with his enemy at her gate had allowed other ladies ample time to prepare for callers—and to receive them. Sadly he went from house to house, finding that he had been preceded in one after the other. Altogether his hand for the cotillon was declined eleven times that afternoon on the legitimate ground of previous engagement. This, with Marjorie, scored off all except five of the seventeen possible partners; and four of the five were also sealed away from him, as he learned in chance encounters with other boys upon the street.

One lady alone remained; he bowed to the inevitable and entered this lorn damsel's gate at twilight with an air of great discouragement. The lorn damsel was Miss Rennsdale, aged eight.

We are apt to forget that there are actually times of life when too much youth is a handicap. Miss Rennsdale was beautiful; she danced like a première; she had every charm but age. On that account alone had she been allowed so much time to prepare to receive callers that it was only by the most manful efforts she could keep her lip from trembling.

A decorous maid conducted the long-belated applicant to her where she sat upon a sofa beside a nursery governess. The decorous maid announced him composedly as he made his entrance.

"Mr. Penrod Schofield!"

Miss Rennsdale suddenly burst into loud sobs.

"Oh!" she wailed. "I just knew it would be him!"

The decorous maid's composure vanished at once—likewise her decorum. She clapped her hand over her mouth and fled, uttering sounds. The governess, however, set herself to comfort her heartbroken charge, and presently succeeded in restoring Miss Rennsdale to a semblance of that poise with which a lady receives callers and accepts invitations to dance cotillons. But she continued to sob at intervals.

Feeling himself at perhaps a disadvantage, Penrod made offer of his hand for the morrow with a little embarrassment. Following the form prescribed by Professor Bartet, he advanced several paces toward the stricken lady and bowed formally.

"I hope," he said by rote, "you're well, and your parents also in good health. May I have the pleasure of dancing the cotillon as your partner t'-morrow afternoon?"

The wet eyes of Miss Rennsdale searched his countenance without pleasure, and a shudder wrung her small shoulders; but the governess whispered to her instructively, and she made a great effort.

"I thu-thank you fu-for your polite invu-invu-invutation; and I ac——" Thus far she progressed when emotion overcame her again. She beat frantically upon the sofa with fists and heels. "Oh, I *did* want it to be Georgie Bassett!"

"No, no, no!" said the governess, and whispered urgently, whereupon Miss Rennsdale was able to complete her acceptance.

"And I ac-accept wu-with pu-pleasure!" she moaned, and immediately, uttering a loud yell, flung herself face downward upon the sofa, clutching her governess convulsively.

Somewhat disconcerted, Penrod bowed again.

"I thank you for your polite acceptance," he murmured hurriedly; "and I trust—I trust—I forget. Oh, yes—I trust we shall have a most enjoyable occasion. Pray present my compliments to your parents; and I must now wish you a very good afternoon."

Concluding these courtly demonstrations with another bow he withdrew in fair order, though thrown into partial confusion in the hall by a final wail from his crushed hostess:

"Oh! Why couldn't it be anybody but *him!*"

MORE ALARMS AT NIGHT by James Thurber

ONE of the incidents that I always think of first when I cast back over my youth is what happened the night that my father "threatened to get Buck." This, as you will see, is not precisely a fair or accurate description of what actually occurred, but it is the way in which I and the other members of my family invariably allude to the occasion. We were living at the time in an old house at 77 Lexington Avenue, in Columbus, Ohio. In the early years of the nineteenth century, Columbus won out, as state capital, by only one vote over Lancaster, and ever since then has had the hallucination that it is being followed, a curious municipal state of mind which affects, in some way or other, all those who live there. Columbus is a town in which almost anything is likely to happen and in which almost everything has.

My father was sleeping in the front room on the second floor next to that of my brother Roy, who was then about sixteen. Father was usually in bed by nine-thirty and up again by ten-thirty to protest bitterly against a Victrola record we three boys were in the habit of playing over and over, namely, "No News, or

What Killed the Dog," a recitation by Nat Wills. The record had been played so many times that its grooves were deeply cut and the needle often kept revolving in the same groove, repeating over and over the same words. Thus: "ate some burnt hoss flesh, ate some burnt hoss flesh, ate some burnt hoss flesh." It was this reiteration that generally got father out of bed.

On the night in question, however, we had all gone to bed at about the same time, without much fuss. Roy, as a matter of fact, had been in bed all day with a kind of mild fever. It wasn't severe enough to cause delirium and my brother was the last person in the world to give way to delirium. Nevertheless, he had warned father when father went to bed, that he *might* become delirious.

About three o'clock in the morning, Roy, who was wakeful, decided to pretend that delirium was on him, in order to have, as he later explained it, some "fun." He got out of bed and, going to my father's room, shook him and said, "Buck, your time has come!" My father's name was not Buck but Charles, nor had he ever been called Buck. He was a tall, mildly nervous, peaceable gentleman, given to quiet pleasures, and eager that everything should run smoothly. "Hmm?" he said, with drowsy bewilderment. "Get up, Buck," said my brother, coldly, but with a certain gleam in his eyes. My father leaped out of bed, on the side away from his son, rushed from the room, locked the door behind him, and shouted us all up.

We were naturally enough reluctant to believe that Roy, who was quiet and self-contained, had threatened his father with any such abracadabra as father said he had. My older brother, Herman, went back to bed without any comment. "You've had a bad dream," my mother said. This vexed my father. "I tell you he called me Buck and told me my time had come," he said. We went to the door of his room, unlocked it, and tiptoed through it to Roy's room. He lay in his bed, breathing easily, as if he were fast asleep. It was apparent at a glance that he did not have a high fever. My mother gave my father a look. "I tell you he did," whispered father.

Our presence in the room finally seemed to awaken Roy and he was (or rather, as we found out long afterward, pretended to be) astonished and bewildered. "What's the matter?" he asked. "Nothing," said my mother. "Just your father had a nightmare." "I did not have a nightmare," said father, slowly and firmly. He wore an old-fashioned, "side-slit" nightgown which looked rather odd on his tall, spare figure. The situation, before we let it drop and everybody went back to bed again, became, as such situations in our family usually did, rather more complicated than ironed out. Roy demanded to know what had happened, and my mother told him, in considerably garbled fashion, what father had told her. At this a light dawned in Roy's eyes. "Dad's got it backward," he said. He then explained that he had heard father get out of bed and had called to him. "I'll handle this," his father had answered. "Buck is downstairs." "Who is this Buck?" my mother demanded of father. "I don't know any Buck and I never said that," father contended, irritably. None of us (except Roy, of course) believed him. "You had a dream," said mother. "People have these dreams." "I did not have a dream," father said. He was pretty well nettled by this time, and he stood in front of a bureau mirror, brushing his hair with a pair of military brushes; it always seemed to calm father to brush his hair. My mother declared that it was "a sin and a shame" for a grown man to wake up a sick boy simply because he (the grown man: father) had got on his back and had a bad dream. My father, as a matter of fact, *had* been known to have nightmares, usually about Lillian Russell and President Cleveland, who chased him.

We argued the thing for perhaps another half-hour, after which mother made father sleep in her room. "You're all safe now, boys," she said, firmly, as she shut her door. I could hear father grumbling for a long time, with an occasional monosyllable of doubt from mother.

It was some six months after this that father went through a similar experience with me. He was at that time sleeping in the room next to mine. I had been trying all afternoon, in vain, to think of the name Perth Amboy. It seems now like a very simple name to recall and yet on the day in question I thought of every other town in the country, as well as such words and names and phrases as terra cotta, Walla-Walla, bill of lading, vice versa, hoity-toity, Pall Mall, Bodley Head, Schumann-Heink, etc., without even coming close to Perth Amboy. I suppose terra cotta was the closest I came, although it was not very close.

Long after I had gone to bed, I was struggling with

the problem. I began to indulge in the wildest fancies as I lay there in the dark, such as that there was no such town, and even that there was no such state as New Jersey. I fell to repeating the word "Jersey" over and over again, until it became idiotic and meaningless. If you have ever lain awake at night and repeated one word over and over, thousands and millions and hundreds of thousands of millions of times, you know the disturbing mental state you can get into. I got to thinking that there was nobody else in the world but me, and various other wild imaginings of that nature. Eventually, lying there thinking these outlandish thoughts, I grew slightly alarmed. I began to suspect that one might lose one's mind over some such trivial mental tic as a futile search for terra firma Piggly Wiggly Gorgonzola Prester John Arc de Triomphe Holy Moses Lares and Penates. I began to feel the imperative necessity of human contact. This silly and alarming tangle of thought and fancy had gone far enough. I might get into some kind of mental aberrancy unless I found out the name of that Jersey town and could go to sleep. Therefore, I got out of bed, walked into the room where father was sleeping, and shook him. "Um?" he mumbled. I shook him more fiercely and he finally woke up, with a glaze of dream and apprehension in his eyes. "What's matter?" he asked, thickly. I must, indeed, have been rather wild of eye, and my hair, which is unruly, becomes monstrously tousled and snarled at night. "Wha's it?" said my father, sitting up, in readiness to spring out of bed on the far side. The thought must have been going through his mind that all his sons were crazy, or on the verge of going crazy. I see that now, but I didn't then, for I had forgotten the Buck incident and did not realize how similar my appearance must have been to Roy's the night he called father Buck and told him his time had come. "Listen," I said. "Name some towns in New Jersey quick!" It must have been around three in the morning. Father got up, keeping the bed between him and me, and started to pull his trousers on. "Don't bother about dressing," I said. "Just name some towns in New Jersey." While he hastily pulled on his clothes —I remember he left his socks off and put his shoes on his bare feet—father began to name, in a shaky voice, various New Jersey cities. I can still see him reaching for his coat without taking his eyes off me. "Newark," he said, "Jersey City, Atlantic City, Elizabeth, Paterson, Passaic, Trenton, Jersey City, Trenton, Paterson—" "It has two names," I snapped. "Elizabeth and Paterson," he said. "No, no!" I told him irritably. "This is one town with one name, but there are two words in it, like helter-skelter." "Helter-skelter," said my father, moving slowly toward the bedroom door and smiling in a faint, strained way which I understand now—but didn't then—was meant to humor me. When he was within a few paces of the door, he fairly leaped for it and ran out into the hall, his coat-tails and shoelaces flying. The exit stunned me. I had no notion that he thought I had gone out of my senses; I could only believe that he had gone out of *his* or that, only partially awake, he was engaged in some form of running in his sleep. I ran after him and I caught him at the door of

mother's room and grabbed him, in order to reason with
him. I shook him a little, thinking to wake him completely. "Mary! Roy! Herman!" he shouted. I, too,
began to shout for my brothers and my mother. My
mother opened her door instantly, and there we were
at 3:30 in the morning grappling and shouting, father
partly dressed, but without socks or shirt, and I in
pajamas.

"*Now*, what?" demanded mother, grimly, pulling
us apart. She was capable, fortunately, of handling any
two of us and she never in her life was alarmed by the
words or actions of any one of us.

"Look out for Jamie!" said father. (He always
called me Jamie when excited.) My mother looked at
me.

"What's the matter with your father?" she demanded.
I said I didn't know; I said he had got up suddenly and
dressed and ran out of the room.

"Where did you think you were going?" mother
asked him, coolly. He looked at me. We looked at each
other, breathing hard, but somewhat calmer.

"He was babbling about New Jersey at this infernal
hour of the night," said father. "He came to my room
and asked me to name towns in New Jersey," Mother
looked at me.

"I just asked him," I said. "I was trying to think of
one and couldn't sleep."

"You see?" said father, triumphantly. Mother didn't
look at him.

"Get to bed, both of you," she said. "I don't want
to hear any more out of you tonight. Dressing and

tearing up and down the hall at this hour in the morning!" She went back into the room and shut her door. Father and I went back to bed. "Are you all right?" he called to me. "Are you?" I asked. "Well, good night," he said. "Good night," I said.

Mother would not let the rest of us discuss the affair next morning at breakfast. Herman asked what the hell had been the matter. "We'll go on to something more elevating," said mother.

## PHILIP WEDGE by E. B. White

To the friends of Philip Wedge, his gradual withdrawal
from human society was the cause of some wonderment.
Most of them were bothered less by his having re-
nounced the world than by their not knowing why.
One explanation was that he had taken up with a
woman. A few people said money had something to
do with it.

Both explanations were absurd. I knew Wedge well,
and got wind of some of the little matters that eventually drove him into a kind of retirement. For one thing,
he had a curious feeling in regard to his nose, being
often troubled with the suspicion that there was a black
smudge on the side of it. This suspicion was usually
groundless, but used to attack him suddenly, unsettling
him and causing him embarrassment and physical discomfort. I have seen him, dining with a large company,
twist quickly in his chair and point questioningly at his
nose. Assured by the person next to him that the nose
was spotless, he would remain uneasy and would close
first one eye, then the other, in an attempt to peer downward and sideways at the suspected member. After
almost throwing his eyeballs out of their sockets, he

would dip his napkin fiercely in a tumbler and dab hard at his nose, reddening it and surprising the whole company.

That was only one thing that troubled him. He was also subject to the suspicion that he had feathers on his back. One of a group of persons in a drawing-room, he would without warning throw his right hand desperately over his left shoulder, and flick at his back, in real terror. This feeling was not without some basis in fact, for at one time the pillow in his bed had developed a leak and for a period of about a week he had found feathers here and there on his person. The pillow had been discarded, of course, but he seemed unable to forget the feathers, and never could believe he was quite without them.

Wedge had difficulty keeping appointments—a failing which further explains his reclusion. He was at heart a romantic fellow and had built up a strange myth about the telephone: he could not bear to think of its ringing when he was not there to answer it, lest the message be one which might change the whole course of his life. His modest apartment was on the fourth floor, and he once told me that he never left it—to keep a date or for any other reason—but that he felt, after shutting the door, that the phone was ringing. Sometimes the suspicion did not take hold of him until he was down three flights of stairs, when he would turn and spring like a goat back up the stairs, fumble madly with his key, and burst into the room to find all quiet. Often this furious ascent would so derange his clothes that he would have to make a complete change, and once or twice, he confided, it had so exhausted him that he had to lie down.

I can't help thinking that Wedge's pet turtle had something to do with his taking the veil. He kept the little beast in an old photograph-developer pan, and fed it bits of beef which he brought from restaurants as often as he remembered to. Unfortunately, he had never devised a satisfactory method of carrying the morsels home, but almost invariably wrapped them in his handkerchief when he thought no one was looking, and replaced the handkerchief in his hip-pocket. This would have been a decent enough expedient had Wedge always gone directly home from the restaurant, but frequently he was diverted, and I happen to know of several occasions when he pulled out his handkerchief— in the lobby of a theatre, in a club, in a cab—and out dropped beef on the floor. Rather than admit to owning a turtle, Wedge preferred to let the matter stand without any explanation; but it unnerved him, and people never understood.

He was a nervous person, anyway. I recall (now that I'm thinking about these things) a day, probably three years ago, when he and I were walking together down Sixth Avenue. As we passed a letter-box, Wedge dropped a letter in—a slight incident which I thought nothing of until, a block later, Wedge suddenly turned and darted back along the sidewalk, twisting and turning and looking from the rear very like a madman. When he reached the letter-box, he seized the slot and jiggled it viciously a dozen times, glancing in finally to see that it was empty. When he joined me again he seemed tired and spent. He told me, in a jerky, shy manner, that he frequently was bothered by the fear that his letter had not been properly posted, and found it necessary to rush back and make sure that it had dropped all the way down into the box.

I shall not call up all Wedge's peculiarities; yet I can hardly omit mention of his phobia about oranges and grapefruit. He delighted in the taste of citrus fruits, and preferred to eat them with a spoon rather than drink the juice; yet I know for a fact that he could not get halfway through an orange without imagining that he had swallowed a pit. The moment this thought took hold of him, he laid down his spoon and puckered his throat into a bad knot, trying to reclaim the imaginary object from his esophagus. This set him against oranges and disturbed his digestion. When other persons were present at table, their astonishment increased his agony.

For all the absurdity of these fears, I suspect Wedge would still not have isolated himself from society had it not been for another peculiarity of his—which I shall explain as delicately as I can. (He told me the main facts himself, so I am not guessing.) At various times in his life, Wedge had courted ladies, with rather a positive grace for so excitable a man. And of course, in going about, he had had occasion to kiss many of them —which he managed with more amiability than passion. By dint of confining his affectionate regard to one lady at a time, and to none very long, he managed to come through his affairs with no very great remorse or em-barrassment. Shortly before his renunciation of society, he was kissing a fine woman in a perfectly creditable manner when (possibly as a result of a phrase he had read somewhere and remembered) the suspicion overcame him that his consort had opened her eyes, in the midst of the kiss, and was calmly regarding him. There was no way definitely to confirm or disprove the suspicion, for Wedge felt that he was ethically unwarranted in opening his own eyes, as well as biologically incapable of it. Therefore, the suspicion remained to trouble him and make all further companionship with the opposite sex unthinkable.

He now lives quietly with his turtle. By divorcing his friends he has probably added to his tranquillity; and I suspect he hasn't changed much but still goes about dabbing his nose, whacking feathers from his back, rushing upstairs to a silent and scornful telephone, jiggling letter-boxes, choking over his orange, and pulling from his hip-pocket a handkerchief from which falls a little morsel of beef. I rather liked him.

## UNCLE FRED FLITS BY by P. G. Wodehouse

In order that they might enjoy their after-luncheon coffee in peace, the Crumpet had taken the guest whom he was entertaining at the Drones Club to the smaller and less frequented of the two smoking-rooms. In the other, he explained, though the conversation always touched an exceptionally high level of brilliance, there was apt to be a good deal of sugar thrown about.

The guest said he understood.

"Young blood, eh?"

"That's right. Young blood."

"And animal spirits."

"And animal, as you say, spirits," agreed the Crumpet. "We get a fairish amount of those here."

"The complaint, however, is not, I observe, universal."

"Eh?"

The other drew his host's attention to the doorway, where a young man in form-fitting tweeds had just appeared. The aspect of this young man was haggard. His eyes glared wildly and he sucked at an empty cigarette-holder. If he had a mind, there was something on it. When the Crumpet called to him to come and join the party, he merely shook his head in a distraught sort of way and disappeared, looking like a character out of a Greek tragedy pursued by the Fates.

The Crumpet sighed.

"Poor old Pongo!"

"Pongo?"

"That was Pongo Twistleton. He's all broken up about his Uncle Fred."

"Dead?"

"No such luck. Coming up to London again tomorrow. Pongo had a wire this morning."

"And that upsets him?"

"Naturally. After what happened last time."

"What was that?"

"Ah!" said the Crumpet.

"What happened last time?"

"You may well ask."

"I do ask."

"Ah!" said the Crumpet.

Poor old Pongo (said the Crumpet) has often discussed his Uncle Fred with me, and if there weren't tears in his eyes when he did so, I don't know a tear in the eye when I see one. In round numbers the Earl of Ickenham, of Ickenham Hall, Ickenham, Hants, he lives in the country most of the year, but from time to time has a nasty way of slipping his collar and getting loose and descending upon Pongo at his flat in the Albany. And every time he does so, the unhappy young blighter is subjected to some soul-testing experience. Because the trouble with this uncle is that, though sixty if a day, he becomes on arriving in the metropolis as young as he feels—which is, apparently, a youngish twenty-two. I don't know if you happen to know what the word "excesses" means, but those are what Pongo's Uncle Fred from the country, when in London, invariably commits.

It wouldn't so much matter, mind you, if he would confine his activities to the club premises. We're pretty broad-minded here, and if you stop short of smashing the piano, there isn't much you can do at the Drones that will cause the raised eyebrow and the sharp intake of breath. The snag is that he will insist on lugging Pongo out in the open and there, right in the public eye, proceeding to step high, wide and plentiful.

So when, on the occasion to which I allude, he stood pink and genial on Pongo's hearth-rug, bulging with Pongo's lunch and wreathed in the smoke of one of Pongo's cigars, and said: "And now, my boy, for a pleasant and instructive afternoon," you will readily understand why the unfortunate young clam gazed at him as he would have gazed at two-penn'orth of dynamite, had he discovered it lighting up in his presence.

"A what?" he said, giving at the knees and paling beneath the tan a bit.

"A pleasant and instructive afternoon," repeated Lord Ickenham, rolling the words round his tongue. "I propose that you place yourself in my hands and leave the programme entirely to me."

Now, owing to Pongo's circumstances being such as to necessitate his getting into the aged relative's ribs at intervals and shaking him down for an occasional much-needed tenner or what not, he isn't in a position to use the iron hand with the old buster. But at these words he displayed a manly firmness.

"You aren't going to get me to the dog races again."

"No, no."

"You remember what happened last June."

"Quite," said Lord Ickenham, "quite. Though I still think that a wiser magistrate would have been content with a mere reprimand."

"And I won't—"

"Certainly not. Nothing of that kind at all. What I propose to do this afternoon is to take you to visit the home of your ancestors."

Pongo did not get this.

"I thought Ickenham was the home of my ancestors."

"It is one of the homes of your ancestors. They also resided rather nearer the heart of things, at a place called Mitching Hill."

"Down in the suburbs, do you mean?"

"The neighborhood is now suburban, true. It is many years since the meadows where I sported as a child were sold and cut up into building lots. But when I was a boy Mitching Hill was open country. It was a vast, rolling estate belonging to your great-uncle, Marma-duke, a man with whiskers of a nature which you with your pure mind would scarcely credit, and I have long felt a sentimental urge to see what the hell the old place looks like now. Perfectly foul, I expect. Still, I think we should make the pious pilgrimage."

Pongo absolutely-ed heartily. He was all for the

scheme. A great weight seemed to have rolled off his mind. The way he looked at it was that even an uncle within a short jump of the looney bin couldn't very well get into much trouble in a suburb. I mean, you know what suburbs are. They don't, as it were, offer the scope. One follows his reasoning, of course.

"Fine!" he said. "Splendid! Topping!"

"Then put on your hat and rompers, my boy," said Lord Ickenham, "and let us be off. I fancy one gets there by omnibuses and things."

Well, Pongo hadn't expected much in the way of mental uplift from the sight of Mitching Hill, and he didn't get it. Alighting from the bus, he tells me, you found yourself in the middle of rows and rows of semi-detached villas, all looking exactly alike, and you went on and you came to more semi-detached villas, and those all looked exactly alike, too. Nevertheless, he did not repine. It was one of those early spring days which suddenly change to mid-winter and he had come out without his overcoat, and it looked like rain and he hadn't an umbrella, but despite this his mood was one of sober ecstasy. The hours were passing and his uncle had not yet made a goat of himself. At the Dog Races the other had been in the hands of the constabulary in the first ten minutes.

It began to seem to Pongo that with any luck he might be able to keep the old blister pottering harmlessly about here till nightfall, when he could shoot a bit of dinner into him and put him to bed. And as Lord Ickenham had specifically stated that his wife, Pongo's

Aunt Jane, had expressed her intention of scalping him with a blunt knife if he wasn't back at the Hall by lunch time on the morrow, it really looked as if he might get through this visit without perpetrating a single major outrage on the public weal. It is rather interesting to note that as he thought this Pongo smiled, because it was the last time he smiled that day.

All this while, I should mention, Lord Ickenham had been stopping at intervals like a pointing dog and saying that it must have been just about here that he plugged the gardener in the trousers seat with his bow and arrow and that over there he had been sick after his first cigar, and he now paused in front of a villa which for some unknown reason called itself The Cedars. His face was tender and wistful.

"On this very spot, if I am not mistaken," he said, heaving a bit of a sigh, "on this very spot, fifty years ago come Lammas Eve, I . . . Oh, blast it!"

The concluding remark had been caused by the fact that the rain, which had held off until now, suddenly began to buzz down like a shower-bath. With no further words, they leaped into the porch of the villa and there took shelter, exchanging glances with a grey parrot which hung in a cage in the window.

Not that you could really call it shelter. They were protected from above all right, but the moisture was now falling with a sort of swivel action, whipping in through the sides of the porch and tickling them up properly. And it was just after Pongo had turned up his collar and was huddling against the door that the door gave way. From the fact that a female of general-

servant aspect was standing there he gathered that his
uncle must have rung the bell.

This female wore a long mackintosh, and Lord
Ickenham beamed upon her with a fairish spot of
suavity.

"Good afternoon," he said.

The female said good afternoon.

"The Cedars?"

The female said yes, it was The Cedars.

"Are the old folks at home?"

The female said there was nobody at home.

"Ah? Well, never mind. I have come," said Lord
Ickenham, edging in, "to clip the parrot's claws. My
assistant, Mr. Walkinshaw, who applies the anaesthetic,"
he added, indicating Pongo with a gesture.

"Are you from the bird shop?"

"A very happy guess."

"Nobody told me you were coming."

"They keep things from you, do they?" said Lord
Ickenham, sympathetically. "Too bad."

Continuing to edge, he had got into the parlour by
now, Pongo following in a sort of dream and the
female following Pongo.

"Well, I suppose it's all right," she said. "I was just
going out. It's my afternoon."

"Go out," said Lord Ickenham cordially. "By all
means go out. We will leave everything in order."

And presently the female, though still a bit on the
dubious side, pushed off, and Lord Ickenham lit the
gas-fire and drew a chair up.

"So here we are, my boy," he said. "A little tact,

a little address, and here we are, snug and cosy and not catching our deaths of cold. You'll never go far wrong if you leave things to me."

"But, dash it, we can't stop here," said Pongo.

Lord Ickenham raised his eyebrows.

"Not stop here? Are you suggesting that we go out into that rain? My dear lad, you are not aware of the grave issues involved. This morning, as I was leaving home, I had a rather painful disagreement with your aunt. She said the weather was treacherous and wished me to take my woolly muffler. I replied that the weather was not treacherous and that I would be dashed if I took my woolly muffler. Eventually, by the exercise of an iron will, I had my way, and I ask you, my dear boy, to envisage what will happen if I return with a cold in the head. I shall sink to the level of a fifth-class power. Next time I came to London, it would be with a liver pad and a respirator. No! I shall remain here, toasting my toes at this really excellent fire. I had no idea that gas-fire radiated such warmth. I feel all in a glow."

So did Pongo. His brow was wet with honest sweat. He is reading for the Bar, and while he would be the first to admit that he hasn't yet got a complete toe-hold on the Law of Great Britain he had a sort of notion that oiling into a perfect stranger's semi-detached villa on the pretext of pruning the parrot was a tort or mis-demeanour, if not actual barratry or soccage in fief or something like that. And apart from the legal aspect of the matter there was the embarrassment of the thing. Nobody is more of a whale on correctness and not doing what's not done than Pongo, and the situation in which he now found himself caused him to chew the lower lip and, as I say, perspire a goodish deal.

"But suppose the blighter who owns this ghastly house comes back?" he asked. "Talking of envisaging things, try that one over on your pianola."

And, sure enough, as he spoke, the front door bell rang.

"There!" said Pongo.

"Don't say 'There!' my boy," said Lord Ickenham reprovingly. "It's the sort of thing your aunt says. I see no reason for alarm. Obviously this is some casual caller. A ratepayer would have used his latchkey. Glance cautiously out of the window and see if you can see anybody."

"It's a pink chap," said Pongo, having done so.

"How pink?"

"Pretty pink."

"Well, there you are, then. I told you so. It can't be the big chief. The sort of fellows who own houses like this are pale and sallow, owing to working in offices all day. Go and see what he wants."

"You go and see what he wants."

"We'll both go and see what he wants," said Lord Ickenham.

So they went and opened the front door, and there, as Pongo had said, was a pink chap. A small young pink chap, a bit moist about the shoulder-blades.

"Pardon me," said this pink chap, "is Mr. Roddis in?"

"No," said Pongo.

"Yes," said Lord Ickenham. "Don't be silly, Douglas

—of course I'm in. I am Mr. Roddis," he said to the pink chap. "This, such as he is, is my son Douglas. And you?"

"Name of Robinson."

"What about it?"

"My name's Robinson."

"Oh, *your* name's Robinson? Now we've got it straight. Delighted to see you, Mr. Robinson. Come right in and take your boots off."

They all trickled back to the parlour, Lord Ickenham pointing out objects of interest by the wayside to the chap, Pongo gulping for air a bit and trying to get himself abreast of this new twist in the scenario. His heart was becoming more and more bowed down with weight of woe. He hadn't liked being Mr. Walkinshaw, the anaesthetist, and he didn't like it any better being Roddis Junior. In brief, he feared the worst. It was only too plain to him by now that his uncle had got it thoroughly up his nose and had settled down to one of his big afternoons, and he was asking himself, as he had so often asked himself before, what would the harvest be?

Arrived in the parlour, the pink chap proceeded to stand on one leg and look coy.

"Is Julia here?" he asked, simpering a bit, Pongo says.

"Is she?" said Lord Ickenham to Pongo.

"No," said Pongo.

"No," said Lord Ickenham.

"She wired me she was coming here to-day."

"Ah, then we shall have a bridge four."

The pink chap stood on the other leg.

"I don't suppose you've ever met Julia. Bit of trouble in the family, she gave me to understand."

"It is often the way."

"The Julia I mean is your niece Julia Parker. Or, rather, your wife's niece Julia Parker."

"Any niece of my wife is a niece of mine," said Lord Ickenham heartily. "We share and share alike."

"Julia and I want to get married."

"Well, go ahead."

"But they won't let us."

"Who won't?"

"Her mother and father. And Uncle Charlie Parker and Uncle Henry Parker and the rest of them. They don't think I'm good enough."

"The morality of the modern young man is notoriously lax."

"Class enough, I mean. They're a haughty lot."

"What makes them haughty? Are they earls?"

"No, they aren't earls."

"Then why the devil," said Lord Ickenham warmly, "are they haughty?" Only earls have a right to be haughty. Earls are hot stuff. When you get an earl, you've got something."

"Besides, we've had words. Me and her father. One thing led to another, and in the end I called him a perishing old—Coo!" said the pink chap, breaking off suddenly.

He had been standing by the window, and he now leaped lissomely into the middle of the room, causing Pongo, whose nervous system was by this time definitely down among the wines and spirits and who hadn't been expecting this *adagio* stuff, to bite his tongue with some severity.

"They're on the doorstep! Julia and her mother and father. I didn't know they were all coming."

"You do not wish to meet them?"

"No, I don't!"

"Then duck behind the settee, Mr. Robinson," said Lord Ickenham, and the pink chap, weighing the advice and finding it good, did so. And as he disappeared the door bell rang.

Once more, Lord Ickenham led Pongo out into the hall.

"I say!" said Pongo, and a close observer might have noted that he was quivering like an aspen.

"Say on, my dear boy."

"I mean to say, what?"

"What?"

"You aren't going to let these bounders in, are you?"

"Certainly," said Lord Ickenham. "We Roddises keep open house. And as they are presumably aware that Mr. Roddis has no son, I think we had better return to the old layout. You are the local vet, my boy, come to minister to my parrot. When I return, I should like to find you by the cage, staring at the bird in a scientific manner. Tap your teeth from time to time with a pencil and try to smell of iodoform. It will help to add conviction."

So Pongo shifted back to the parrot's cage and stared so earnestly that it was only when a voice said "Well!" that he became aware that there was anybody in the

room. Turning, he perceived that Hampshire's leading
curse had come back, bringing the gang.

It consisted of a stern, thin, middle-aged woman, a
middle-aged man and a girl.

You can generally accept Pongo's estimate of girls,
and when he says that this one was a pippin one knows
that he uses the term in its most exact sense. She was
about nineteen, he thinks, and she wore a black beret,
a dark-green leather coat, a shortish tweed skirt, silk
stockings and high-heeled shoes. Her eyes were large
and lustrous and her face like a dewy rosebud at daybreak on a June morning. So Pongo tells me. Not that
I suppose he has ever seen a rosebud at daybreak on a
June morning, because it's generally as much as you can
do to lug him out of bed in time for nine-thirty breakfast. Still, one gets the idea.

"Well," said the woman, "you don't know who I am,
I'll be bound. I'm Laura's sister Connie. This is Claude,
my husband. And this is my daughter Julia. Is Laura
in?"

"I regret to say, no," said Lord Ickenham.

The woman was looking at him as if he didn't come
up to her specifications.

"I thought you were younger," she said.

"Younger than what?" said Lord Ickenham.

"Younger than you are."

"You can't be younger than you are, worse luck,"
said Lord Ickenham. "Still, one does one's best, and I
am bound to say that of recent years I have made a
pretty good go of it."

The woman caught sight of Pongo, and he didn't seem to please her, either.

"Who's that?"

"The local vet, clustering round my parrot."

"I can't talk in front of him."

"It is quite all right," Lord Ickenham assured her. "The poor fellow is stone deaf."

And with an imperious gesture at Pongo, as much as to bid him stare less at girls and more at parrots, he got the company seated.

"Now, then," he said.

There was silence for a moment, then a sort of muffled sob, which Pongo thinks proceeded from the girl. He couldn't see, of course, because his back was turned and he was looking at the parrot, which looked back at him—most offensively, he says, as parrots will, using one eye only for the purpose. It also asked him to have a nut.

The woman came into action again.

"Although," she said, "Laura never did me the honour to invite me to her wedding, for which reason I have not communicated with her for five years, necessity compels me to cross her threshold to-day. There comes a time when differences must be forgotten and relatives must stand shoulder to shoulder."

"I see what you mean," said Lord Ickenham. "Like the boys of the old brigade."

"What I say is, let bygones be bygones. I would not have intruded on you, but needs must. I disregard the past and appeal to your sense of pity."

The thing began to look to Pongo like a touch, and

he is convinced that the parrot thought so, too, for it winked and cleared its throat. But they were both wrong. The woman went on.

"I want you and Laura to take Julia into your home for a week or so, until I can make other arrangements for her. Julia is studying the piano, and she sits for her examination in two weeks' time, so until then she must remain in London. The trouble is, she has fallen in love. Or thinks she has."

"I know I have," said Julia.

Her voice was so attractive that Pongo was compelled to slew round and take another look at her. Her eyes, he says, were shining like twin stars and there was a sort of Soul's Awakening expression on her face, and what the dickens there was in a pink chap like the pink chap, who even as pink chaps go wasn't much of a pink chap, to make her look like that, was frankly, Pongo says, more than he could understand. The thing baffled him. He sought in vain for a solution.

"Yesterday, Claude and I arrived in London from our Bexhill home to give Julia a pleasant surprise. We stayed, naturally, in the boarding-house where she has been living for the past six weeks. And what do you think we discovered?"

"Insects?"

"Not insects. A letter. From a young man. I found to my horror that a young man of whom I knew nothing was arranging to marry my daughter. I sent for him immediately, and found him to be quite impossible. He jellies eels!"

"Does what?"

"He is an assistant at a jellied eel shop."

"But surely," said Lord Ickenham, "that speaks well for him. The capacity to jelly an eel seems to me to argue intelligence of a high order. It isn't everybody who can do it, by any means. I know if someone came to me and said 'Jelly this eel!' I should be nonplussed. And so, or I am very much mistaken, would Ramsay MacDonald and Winston Churchill."

The woman did not seem to see eye to eye.

"Tchah!" she said. "What do you suppose my husband's brother Charlie Parker would say if I allowed his niece to marry a man who jellies eels?"

"Ah," said Claude, who, before we go any further, was a tall, drooping bird with a red soup-strainer moustache.

"Or my husband's brother, Henry Parker."

"Ah!" said Claude. "Or Cousin Alf Robbins, for that matter."

"Exactly. Cousin Alfred would die of shame."

The girl Julia hiccoughed passionately, so much so that Pongo says it was all he could do to stop himself nipping across and taking her hand in his and patting it.

"I've told you a hundred times, mother, that Wilberforce is only jellying eels till he finds something better."

"What is better than an eel?" asked Lord Ickenham, who had been following this discussion with the close attention it deserved. "For jellying purposes, I mean."

"He is ambitious. It won't be long," said the girl, "before Wilberforce suddenly rises in the world."

She never spoke a truer word. At this very moment, up he came from behind the settee like a leaping salmon.

"Julia!" he cried.

"Wilby!" yipped the girl.

And Pongo says he never saw anything more sickening in his life than the way she flung herself into the blighter's arms and clung there like the ivy on the old garden wall. It wasn't that he had anything specific against the pink chap, but this girl had made a deep impression on him and he resented her gluing herself to another in this manner.

Julia's mother, after just that brief moment which a woman needs in which to recover from her natural surprise at seeing eel-jelliers pop up from behind sofas, got moving and plucked her away like a referee breaking a couple of welter-weights.

"Julia Parker," she said, "I'm ashamed of you!"

"So am I," said Claude.

"I blush for you."

"Me, too," said Claude. "Hugging and kissing a man who called your father a perishing old bottle-nosed Gawd-help-us."

"I think," said Lord Ickenham, shoving his oar in, "that before proceeding any further we ought to go into that point. If he called you a perishing old bottle-nosed Gawd-help-us, it seems to me that the first thing to do is to decide whether he was right, and frankly, in my opinion . . ."

"Wilberforce will apologize."

"Certainly I'll apologize. It isn't fair to hold a remark passed in the heat of the moment against a chap . . ."

"Mr. Robinson," said the woman, "you know per-

fectly well that whatever remarks you may have seen
fit to pass don't matter one way or the other. If you
were listening to what I was saying you will understand . . ."

"Oh, I know, I know. Uncle Charlie Parker and
Uncle Henry Parker and Cousin Alf Robbins and all
that. Pack of snobs!"

"What!"

"Haughty, stuck-up snobs. Them and their class
distinctions. Think themselves everybody just because
they've got money. I'd like to know how they got it."

"What do you mean by that?"

"Never mind what I mean."

"If you are insinuating—"

"Well, of course, you know, Connie," said Lord
Ickenham mildly, "he's quite right. You can't get away
from that."

I don't know if you have ever seen a bull-terrier
embarking on a scrap with an Airedale and just as it was
getting down nicely to its work suddenly having an
unexpected Kerry Blue sneak up behind it and bite it
in the rear quarters. When this happens, it lets go of
the Airedale and swivels round and fixes the butting-in
animal with a pretty nasty eye. It was exactly the same
with the woman Connie when Lord Ickenham spoke
these words.

"What!"

"I was only wondering if you had forgotten how
Charlie Parker made his pile."

"What are you talking about?"

"I know it is painful," said Lord Ickenham, "and one

doesn't mention it as a rule, but, as we are on the subject, you must admit that lending money at two hundred
and fifty per cent interest is not done in the best circles.
The judge, if you remember, said so at the trial."

"I never knew that!" cried the girl Julia.

"Ah," said Lord Ickenham. "You kept it from the
child? Quite right, quite right."

"It's a lie!"

"And when Henry Parker had all that fuss with the
bank it was touch and go they didn't send him to prison.
Between ourselves, Connie, has a bank official, even a
brother of your husband, any right to sneak fifty pounds
from the till in order to put it on a hundred to one shot
for the Grand National? Not quite playing the game,
Connie. Not the straight bat. Henry, I grant you, won
five thousand of the best and never looked back afterwards, but, though we applaud his judgment of form,
we must surely look askance at his financial methods.
As for Cousin Alf Robbins . . ."

The woman was making rummy stuttering sounds.
Pongo tells me he once had a Pommery Seven which
used to express itself in much the same way if you tried
to get it to take a hill on high. A sort of mixture of
gurgles and explosions.

"There is not a word of truth in this," she gasped at
length, having managed to get the vocal cords disen-
tangled. "Not a single word. I think you must have
gone mad."

Lord Ickenham shrugged his shoulders.

"Have it your own way, Connie. I was only going
to say that, while the jury were probably compelled on

the evidence submitted to them to give Cousin Alf
Robbins the benefit of the doubt when charged with
smuggling dope, everybody knew that he had been doing it for years. I am not blaming him, mind you. If a
man can smuggle cocaine and get away with it, good
luck to him, say I. The only point I am trying to make
is that we are hardly a family that can afford to put on
dog and sneer at honest suitors for our daughters' hands.
Speaking for myself, I consider that we are very lucky
to have the chance of marrying even into eel-jellying
circles."

"So do I," said Julia firmly.

"You don't believe what this man is saying?"

"I believe every word."

"So do I," said the pink chap.

The woman snorted. She seemed overwrought.

"Well," she said, "goodness knows I have never liked
Laura, but I would never have wished her a husband
like you!"

"Husband?" said Lord Ickenham, puzzled. "What
gives you the impression that Laura and I are married?"

There was a weighty silence, during which the parrot
threw out a general invitation to the company to join
it in a nut. Then the girl Julia spoke.

"You'll have to let me marry Wilberforce now," she
said. "He knows too much about us."

"I was rather thinking that myself," said Lord Ickenham. "Seal his lips, I say."

"You wouldn't mind marrying into a low family,
would you, darling?" asked the girl, with a touch of
anxiety.

"No family could be too low for me, dearest, if it was yours," said the pink chap.

"After all, we needn't see them."

"That's right."

"It isn't one's relations that matter: it's oneselves."

"That's right, too."

"Wilby!"

"Julia!"

They repeated the old ivy on the garden wall act. Pongo says he didn't like it any better than the first time, but his distaste wasn't in it with the woman Connie's.

"And what, may I ask," she said, "do you propose to marry on?"

This seemed to cast a damper. They came apart. They looked at each other. The girl looked at the pink chap, and the pink chap looked at the girl. You could see that a jarring note had been struck.

"Wilberforce is going to be a very rich man some day."

"Some day!"

"If I had a hundred pounds," said the pink chap, "I could buy a half-share in one of the best milk walks in South London to-morrow."

"If!" said the woman.

"Ah!" said Claude.

"Where are you going to get it?"

"Ah!" said Claude.

"Where," repeated the woman, plainly pleased with the snappy crack and loath to let it ride without an encore, "are you going to get it?"

"That," said Claude, "is the point. Where are you going to get a hundred pounds?"

"Why, bless my soul," said Lord Ickenham jovially, "from me, of course. Where else?"

And before Pongo's bulging eyes he fished out from the recesses of his costume a crackling bundle of notes and handed it over. And the agony of realising that the old bounder had had all that stuff on him all this time and that he hadn't touched him for so much as a tithe of it was so keen, Pongo says, that before he knew what he was doing he had let out a sharp, whinnying cry which rang through the room like the yowl of a stepped-on puppy.

"Ah," said Lord Ickenham. "The vet wishes to speak to me. Yes, vet?"

This seemed to puzzle the cerise bloke a bit.

"I thought you said this chap was your son."

"If I had a son," said Lord Ickenham, a little hurt, "he would be a good deal better-looking than that. No, this is the local veterinary surgeon. I may have said I *looked* on him as a son. Perhaps that was what confused you."

He shifted across to Pongo and twiddled his hands enquiringly. Pongo gaped at him, and it was not until one of the hands caught him smartly in the lower ribs that he remembered he was deaf and started to twiddle back. Considering that he wasn't supposed to be dumb, I can't see why he should have twiddled, but no doubt there are moments when twiddling is about all a fellow feels himself equal to. For what seemed to him at least ten hours Pongo had been undergoing great mental stress, and one can't blame him for not being chatty. Anyway, be that as it may, he twiddled.

"I cannot quite understand what he says," announced Lord Ickenham at length, "because he sprained a finger this morning and that makes him stammer. But I gather that he wishes to have a word with me in private. Possibly my parrot has got something the matter with it which he is reluctant to mention even in sign language in front of a young unmarried girl. You know what parrots are. We will step outside."

"*We* will step outside," said Wilberforce.

"Yes," said the girl Julia. "I feel like a walk."

"And you?" said Lord Ickenham to the woman Connie, who was looking like a female Napoleon at Moscow. "Do you join the hikers?"

"I shall remain and make myself a cup of tea. You will not grudge us a cup of tea, I hope?"

"Far from it," said Lord Ickenham cordially. "This is Liberty Hall. Stick around and mop it up till your eyes bubble."

Outside, the girl, looking more like a dewy rosebud than ever, fawned on the old buster pretty considerably.

"I don't know how to thank you!" she said. And the pink chap said he didn't, either.

"Not at all, my dear, not at all," said Lord Ickenham.

"I think you're simply wonderful."

"No, no."

"You are. Perfectly marvellous."

"Tut, tut," said Lord Ickenham. "Don't give the matter another thought."

He kissed her on both cheeks, the chin, the forehead,

the right eyebrow, and the tip of the nose, Pongo looking on the while in a baffled and discontented manner. Everybody seemed to be kissing this girl except him.

Eventually the degrading spectacle ceased and the girl and the pink chap shoved off, and Pongo was enabled to take up the matter of that hundred quid.

"Where," he asked, "did you get all that money?"

"Now, where did I?" mused Lord Ickenham. "I know your aunt gave it to me for some purpose. But what? To pay some bill or other, I rather fancy."

This cheered Pongo up slightly.

"She'll give you the devil when you get back," he said, with not a little relish. "I wouldn't be in your shoes for something. When you tell Aunt Jane," he said, with confidence, for he knew his Aunt Jane's emotional nature, "that you slipped her entire roll to a girl, and explain, as you will have to explain, that she was an extraordinarily pretty girl—a girl, in fine, who looked like something out of a beauty chorus of the better sort, I should think she would pluck down one of the ancestral battle-axes from the wall and jolly well strike you on the mazzard."

"Have no anxiety, my dear boy," said Lord Ickenham. "It is like your kind heart to be so concerned, but have no anxiety. I shall tell her that I was compelled to give the money to you to enable you to buy back some compromising letters from a Spanish *demi-mondaine*. She will scarcely be able to blame me for rescuing a fondly-loved nephew from the clutches of an adventuress. It may be that she will feel a little vexed with you for a while, and that you may have to allow a certain time to elapse before you visit Ickenham again, but then I shan't be wanting you at Ickenham till the ratting season starts, so all is well."

At this moment, there came toddling up to the gate of The Cedars a large red-faced man. He was just going in when Lord Ickenham hailed him.

"Mr. Roddis?"

"Hey?"

"Am I addressing Mr. Roddis?"

"That's me."

"I am Mr. J. G. Bulstrode from down the road," said Lord Ickenham. "This is my sister's husband's brother, Percy Frensham, in the lard and imported-butter business."

The red-faced bird said he was pleased to meet them. He asked Pongo if things were brisk in the lard and imported-butter business, and Pongo said they were all right, and the red-faced bird said he was glad to hear it.

"We have never met, Mr. Roddis," said Lord Ickenham, "but I think it would be only neighbourly to inform you that a short while ago I observed two suspicious-looking persons in your house."

"In my house? How on earth did they get there?"

"No doubt through a window at the back. They looked to me like cat burglars. If you creep up, you may be able to see them."

The red-faced bird crept, and came back not exactly foaming at the mouth but with the air of a man who for two pins would so foam.

"You're perfectly right. They're sitting in my

parlour as cool as dammit, swigging my tea and buttered toast."

"I thought as much."

"And they've opened a pot of my raspberry jam."

"Ah, then you will be able to catch them red-handed. I should fetch a policeman."

"I will. Thank you, Mr. Bulstrode."

"Only too glad to have been able to render you this little service, Mr. Roddis," said Lord Ickenham. "Well, I must be moving along. I have an appointment. Pleasant after the rain, is it not? Come, Percy."

He lugged Pongo off.

"So that," he said, with satisfaction, "is that. On these visits of mine to the metropolis, my boy, I always make it my aim, if possible, to spread sweetness and light. I look about me, even in a foul hole like Mitching Hill, and I ask myself—How can I leave this foul hole a better and happier foul hole than I found it? And if I see a chance, I grab it. Here is our omnibus. Spring aboard, my boy, and on our way home we will be sketching out rough plans for the evening. If the old Leicester Grill is still in existence, we might look in there. It must be fully thirty-five years since I was last thrown out of the Leicester Grill. I wonder who is the bouncer there now."

Such (concluded the Crumpet) is Pongo Twistleton's Uncle Fred from the country, and you will have gathered by now a rough notion of why it is that when a telegram comes announcing his impending arrival in the great city Pongo blenches to the core and calls for a couple of quick ones.

The whole situation, Pongo says, is very complex. Looking at it from one angle, it is fine that the man lives in the country most of the year. If he didn't, he would have him in his midst all the time. On the other hand, by living in the country he generates, as it were, a store of loopiness which expends itself with frightful violence on his rare visits to the centre of things.

What it boils down to is this—Is it better to have a loopy uncle whose loopiness is perpetually on tap but spread out thin, so to speak, or one who lies low in distant Hants for three hundred and sixty days in the year and does himself proud in London for the other five? Dashed moot, of course, and Pongo has never been able to make up his mind on the point.

Naturally, the ideal thing would be if someone would chain the old hound up permanently and keep from Jan. One to Dec. Thirty-one where he wouldn't do any harm—viz. among the spuds and tenantry. But this, Pongo admits, is a Utopian dream. Nobody could work harder to that end than his Aunt Jane, and she has never been able to manage it.